GW00655978

IRELAND IN EXILE

IRELAND IN EXILE

Irish Writers Abroad

EDITED BY

DERMOT BOLGER

NEW ISLAND BOOKS

Dublin

IRELAND IN EXILE
is first published in 1993 by
NEW ISLAND BOOKS
2 Brookside
Dundrum Road,
Dublin 14.

ISBN 1 874597 55 3

New Island Books receives financial support of
The Arts Council (An Chomhairle Ealaíon), Dublin, Ireland.

A catalogue record for this book is available from
the British Library.

All works © their respective authors, 1993
See extended notice on pages 174-175
Introduction © Joseph O'Connor, 1993
Foreword and selection © Dermot Bolger, 1993

Typeset by Graphic Resourses, Dublin. Printed and bound in
Ireland by Colour Books Ltd, Baldoyle. Cover design by Jon
Berkeley.

CONTENTS

V1

Foreword

Dermot Bolger

This anthology was originally to be called *Lines of Departure*. The current title, taken from Aidan Hynes' story, seemed more suitable — although in many respects both might be termed equally inaccurate. *Exile* and *departure* suggest an out-dated degree of permanency. Irish writers no longer go into exile, they simply commute. Indeed, one of Emma Donoghue's characters makes the point, in *Going Back*, that "I've felt more an exile for twenty years in Ireland than I ever have in the twelve outside of it."

In contrast to the days when once you were gone you stayed "gone", while editing this anthology my major problem was remembering who was now back and who was away. A few years ago writers, currently Irish based, like Mary Dorcey, Robert McLiam Wilson, Sebastian Barry and so many others would have been definite starters, while writers like Deirdre Madden, Harry Clifton and Rosita Boland would have been excluded as being resident in Ireland. The editorial line that I have taken is of writers *currently outside Ireland*. In reality, within the work of almost every younger Irish writer one could find some piece that would fit into the theme of this book. The experience of Irish life today is as much of London, New York and Paris as it is of Dublin, Derry or Castlebar.

In a letter accompanying his contribution to this anthology Colum McCann summed up this new emigration: *"Of course the nature of emigration has changed for all of us — when London is a one-hour flight away from Knock it's hard to say that we've actually emigrated. Not in the same way as people did before — flocks of wild geese, coffin ships, American wakes. In my travels it's been strange to find an Irishman in virtually every small town I've visited. Just two days ago I was out in the arse-end of Kyushu*

Island when out popped a young man from Limerick. In a town called Goodnight, Texas I met a Cavan man working as a ranch hand. When I bartended in Austin, Texas, there was seldom a week went by when I didn't see a new Irish face..."

In recent years there have been many academic attempts to drive an artificial dividing line in Irish writing between the urban and rural Irish experience. This is a safe exercise in avoidance which is at least twenty years out of date. In truth the difference between life in Dublin and Dingle is minuscule in contrast to life between the arse-end of Castleisland and "the arse-end of Kyushu Island" in Japan, and it is in this gap that the real division in contemporary Irish life — and literature — has existed for far longer than the present decade.

This has been obscured by the terrible silence remarked upon by Joseph O'Connor in relation to the Irish emigration experience. With a few exceptions like Donall Mac Amhlaigh's *Dialann Deoraí* (translated as *An Irish Navvy*), and fictions by the likes of Walter Macken and Edna O'Brien and some others, the experience of that huge section of Irish people who were shipped off abroad, has played little part in Irish literature. The part they did play has frequently been clichéd and looking backwards.

The experience I have wished to have articulated in this anthology is that of a modern Ireland, often at odds not only with the Ireland they have left but also the Ireland (of older Irish emigrants — as in Martin Meenan's story) they have to confront abroad. Obviously such a book can only capture fragments of that experience, and just because the concept of the Irish navvy is clichéd does not mean that he doesn't still very much exist. However he is now as likely to be found building Euro Disney as digging trenches in Kilburn.

It is to be hoped that *Ireland in Exile* will prove, for many Irish readers, an uncomfortable read, that it will touch a raw nerve which has been too long ignored. More importantly, for Irish readers abroad it is hoped that it will, in places, echo and reflect their own experiences and emotional responses to life outside Ireland.

It is divided into a number of loose sections, starting with Harry Clifton's opening line that "where we live no longer matters" and Colum McCann's extraordinary marriage of magic realism and Westmeath.

It moves onto the European experience of Michael O'Loughlin's factory workers in Germany; Glenn Patterson's Northern labourers building Euro Disney (from a novel in progress), Deirdre's Madden's Irish girl in Italy and Tony Keily's futurist *Strands*.

Irish exile in New York is even more defined by divisions in Irish society, for the characters in Aidan Hynes' *The Journey Back*, than when the characters lived in Ireland itself. The same city is the setting for the culture clash in Eamonn Wall's story of an Irish family coming to collect the body of their son, a painter who died of Aids. Aids is also central to Helena Mulkerns' *The Suitcase* — an insight into the twilight mid 1980s illegal world of New York. Finally Colm O'Gaora is narrator returns from America to confront the past of his grandfather, who fought in the Irish War of Independence to establish an Irish state.

The inheritors of that state have come into their own in the extract from Harry Clifton's novel-in-progress, *A Ship Came from Valparaiso*, where a minor Irish politician wallows through the mud and UN red tape of refugee camps in the Far East.

Australia is the destination of the young man passing through London in Sara Berkeley's extract from the central story of her début collection; an experience which is echoed in Rosita Boland's poem about touching down in Sydney, *Arriving*. And finally the Irish experience in London is explored by Joseph O'Connor, Martin Meenan and Emma Donoghue.

This book aims to capture, in their own words, the experience of a new breed of Irish writer abroad — writers who have frequently turned their back on a country which has long since turned its back on them, but whose work is now increasingly a central part of Irish literature. For reasons of space the book can obviously be no more than a sample of that experience. There are many more writers who could be here, like Michael Collins in America, Frank Ronan in France, Padraig Rooney in Japan, Patrick McCabe, Desmond Hogan and Matthew Sweeney in

London — not to mention poets like Greg Delaney in America and Louis de Paor in Australia. Many of these, however, are already well known in their native country, and my concern has been to introduce — alongside familiar names — newer authors who have at times been silenced by distance.

What impresses me most about these writers is a refusal to deal in clichés and a willingness instead to confront the awkwardness of reality — the Irish workers booing a Republican speech in Germany and being attacked by Germans convinced they are English, or the gays in London refusing to hide behind standard pre-decimal myths about Ireland and willing to come back for a Gay Pride March in Dublin.

Ironically the present writer is one of the few writers of his generation not to have lived outside Ireland. This has, in small part in the past, been due to a decision to run a publishing house in Ireland which provided a platform for many writers who did live abroad. With that said, and no more than any other Irish person, I am no stranger to the experience of emigration. My father is from a family of seven, my mother was from one of eleven. Apart from the uncle who kept the farm in Monaghan, on one side, and the uncle who kept the house in Wexford, on the other, every other member of those two families emigrated to, and remained in, Britain. The only exceptions (apart from two early deaths) were for my father and one other uncle. Both of these managed to make homes for their families in Finglas, my uncle by spending a decade of his working life sending money home from car plants in the English Midlands, and my father by leaving Ireland every working week for over forty years as a sailor. The rest of my extended family vanished into a glass wall of silence which is only now finally beginning to be broken. It is my hope that the two fingers on the back of this book have just unleashed one small stone to help in some way to shatter that wall.

Dermot Bolger,
Dublin,
Aug, 1993

JOSEPH O'CONNOR

Introduction

One day when I was in my final year in University College Dublin, a man arrived out from town on the number 10 bus and began to wander around the campus assailing bemused and passing undergraduates. He was a photographer, as it turned out, and he had been commissioned by the Industrial Development Authority to take pictures for an advertisement that would persuade rich foreign capitalists to open factories all over the Irish countryside. He wanted images of handsome and clever-looking students who would be willing to dress up in tweed jackets and Laura Ashley frocks, and peer into the lens of his Leica, and smile and forget about the fact that they would never be able to get jobs in their own country, despite the fact that the PAYE workers of that country had shelled out considerable bucketloads of folding stuff to subsidise their chances of so doing. He wanted young people who would embody, really, the new and thrusting young Ireland that journalists were wittering on about in the papers at the time. Payment was involved, I understand.

Now, there was a good deal of fuss about this photographer. It's a funny thing, but the more education people get, in my experience, the fonder they are of having their photograph taken. I don't know why this should be the case, yet it does seem to be. Everyone wanted to be in this advertisement, anyway, but none of the people I knew got selected. When I think back now on the way myself and my friends tried to look in those days, I suppose I'm not surprised. We did not give good factory, let us say, and I don't think the entrepreneurs would have taken to us one bit. It would have been a little like photographing the high command of the Serbian irregular militia in order to entice investors to come to Bosnia and open a mosque.

11

Some months afterwards, a pal of mine arrived up to my house with a copy of this IDA poster. I think he'd cut it out of a newspaper. The slogan underneath the photo announced, proudly, THE REPUBLIC OF IRELAND: WE'RE THE YOUNG EUROPEANS. As it turned out, my friend knew one of these young Europeans, a very talented engineer from rural Ireland, I believe, who had just upped and offed to Saudi Arabia, having failed after much effort to find employment at home. My pal went through all the faces in the photograph, pointing out to me that this person was in America, that one was in Australia, several were in Spain, or France, or Italy, and, of course, many more were in England. Most of the young people in this poster had fled the country, precisely because of the suicidal economic policies which the same poster was attempting to advertise. Those who were still living in Ireland were unemployed, and in the Summer of 1986, believe me, they had an ice-pop's chance in the Kalahari of finding a job. (There *was* a job sighted in Ireland that Summer alright, somewhere around Portarlington, but when the army was called in to investigate it turned out to be just a mirage, and everyone heaved a sigh of relief.) We talked for a while about this IDA poster, my friend and myself. It seemed an awful pity, I suppose, that all these good-looking young people who were supposed to embody Ireland's brave new image had been forced out of their country to get work. It seemed fierce deep somehow. "Comment on the irony", as the Leaving Certificate English paper would have doubtlessly said.

It's seven years later now, and I've been in London for six of those years. At the time of writing, a version of this IDA advertisement is still running. There's a new slogan on it these days. REPUBLIC OF IRELAND: THE QUALITY BUSINESS BASE IN EUROPE. Not the *best* business base, you notice, nor even the cheapest — which is what the words are actually straining to say — but, meaninglessly enough, the "quality". You see this ad from time to time in the newspapers, or in the glossy magazines that you get on airplanes, the ones with photospreads of Jury's Irish Cabaret and long articles about communes of clapped-out English hippies making revolting cheese and knitting their own knickers down in West Cork. And you always see it in Dublin Airport.

You might be coming home for Christmas, or a family celebration, or a funeral, or to see a friend. Or you might just be coming back to Ireland because you're so lonely and freaked-out where you are that you can't stick it any more, and you need a break, and you'd sell your Granny to be back in the pub at home by nine o'clock on a Friday night, having fun and telling stories.

And there it is, this IDA poster, illuminated at the end of the corridor that leads from the airbridge gates to the arrivals terminal; the ghostly faces of those beautiful Young Europeans. It always seems poignant as any ancient Ulster saga to me, this pantheon of departed heroes, so hopeful and innocent, frozen in their brief moment of optimism.

And you meet your friends the night you get home, the people who stayed behind. You talk to them about what's happening and there's loads of news. Some of them are getting married to people you haven't even met, because you don't live in Ireland any more. Some have broken up with long-time lovers, others are still trying to get decent work. Some of them have had kids you've never seen. You don't really know what these scandals and gobbets of gossip are, about which people are laughing so knowledgeably as they sip their pints, but you laugh too, because you don't want to be left out. You pretend you know what your friends are talking about, because you still want to belong. And sometimes there are rows, as the night wears on, because you don't keep in touch as much as you should, and they resent you a bit for going anyway, and you resent them a bit for staying, although you can't put your finger on why. But the conversation flows, as much as it can, with a couple of awkward moments. When you use the words "home" or "at home", for instance, your friends don't really know what you mean. Sometimes you don't know yourself.

Before you're aware of time passing, it's the middle of a busy Friday night. The pub is full of smoke and the smell of beer, and the juke box is on loud, playing U2 or The Pogues, and the joint is jumping, and you have all your best friends around you, all the people you know and love, and who love you. Everything is fine now. You're home. You know the score. Nothing bad can happen. More drink. Everyone is glad to see you. You're glad to see them. It's familiar. You're home. And then an extremely odd sensation begins.

Suddenly, about half an hour before closing time, you find yourself looking around the pub and becoming frantically uptight. You're feeling completely out of place, you don't know why. It's weird. You don't get it. But somehow, despite the *ceol* and the *caint* and the *craic*, something is wrong. You're home in Ireland, but you're not home really. London is still in your head, or New York, or Paris. But you're in *Ireland*. How did this happen? It's not that you're unhappy exactly. This is where you wanted to be tonight. But it's just not right. You take a swig of your drink, and the music seems louder. You close your eyes and try to fight back the almost *overwhelming* urge to be somewhere — anywhere — else. And you realise in that moment that you really are an emigrant now. And that being an emigrant isn't just an address. You realise that it's actually a way of thinking about Ireland.

A few mornings later you're back at the airport to fly home — ah, that difficult word again — and you're hungover. Your head is pounding with confusion and tension as you say your goodbyes. You embrace your loved ones, say you'll be back soon, although you probably won't. And you see that bloody poster of the Young Europeans once more, on your way back out of the country, on the wall of the corridor that runs parallel to the duty free shop. They stare dolefully down at you, those pure virginal faces, as you shuffle through the plastic racks of Irish whiskey, smoked salmon, Tayto crisps and Major cigarettes, wondering what you'll buy with your mountain of leftover change. Sometimes you ask yourself what on earth they must be thinking, these speculative faces. But you know what *you're* thinking because it's so very simple in the end. You're thinking: *run*. You're thinking: *quick, don't even ponder it. Go. Run. Don't stop. Get out*, just get on that plane and vanish.

We are now, as we have always been, a land of exiles and wanderers. "The history of transport", muses a Paul Durcan poem, "is there any other history?" Well, it's a very Irish question. Ever since Joyce discovered the shortest way to Tara was via Holyhead — a soundbite which I've always thought should be used in a Sealink advertising campaign, preferably intoned in the velvety voice of TV's Mr Frank Delaney — hundreds of thousands of us have followed the unwashed and bright-eyed Stephen Dedalus, on that heartbreaking, exhilarating and, frequently, stomach-churning journey across the snotgreen sea.

Emigration has changed, admittedly, over the years. The sons and daughters of the middle classes emigrate now, in search of higher wages and career prospects. They fly back home at weekends to parties in Killiney and Montenotte, these young successful people of the Ryanair generation. Their parents think it's good for them to be out of Ireland for a while, think it broadens their minds. It probably does.

But we also continue to export our poor, our uneducated, our weak. We throw out our suffering, our homeless, those who are as utterly dispossessed in their own country as any refusenik. We expel those who are inconvenient to our fabulous dream of ourselves. That dream used to be of a post-revolutionary Celtic Erin, where we would all be rural, Catholic, heterosexual, conservative, in a family as nuclear as The Waltons, where we would all know our places, respect our betters, wear Aran jumpers, smoke pipes and write turgid poetry in Irish about fishermen. Yeats said independent Ireland would be no country for old men, but how breathtakingly, unusually wrong he was. For the last seventy years that's precisely what it's been. A country where being old and male really does clock up points.

More recently, the dream has been of a post-Maastricht, utterly dehistorified tax-haven, with sixteen channels of satellite TV, full employment at slave pay in prefabricated factories, and smooth new roads paid for by the Germans. Things are changing now, we can all see it. Ireland is introducing civilised laws, recognising that it needs to be humane in its social arrangements. Some of the emigrants I know will go back. But for others, it's too late. They feel that dreams change, but in Ireland waking up is always the same. Always was, always will be. Which is why they like waking up somewhere else.

Emigration is as Irish as Cathleen Ni Houlihan's harp, yet it is only since the sixties and the generation of Edna O'Brien that Irish writers have written about the subject at first hand. That seems staggering, I know, but I think it is true. It has been taken as read that Exile is an important theme in Irish writing, like The Big House or The Catholic Church. But if it is, it's an inconsistent and entirely intermittent preoccupation. Where are the first-person texts of Irish emigrant life in the latter part of the last century and the earlier part of this? With one or two exceptions — Robert Tressel's *Ragged Trousered Philanthropists*, say, and the bleak spare poems of Patrick Magill — they're not there. At the heart of the Irish emigrant experience there is a caution, a refusal to speak, a fear of the word.

Our emigrant culture has traditionally been described in songs rather than novels, plays or poems. But a friend of mine said to me recently that he was sure all those sententiously vile ballads about dear little shamrocks, grey-haired macushlas and shagging shillelaghs were written by people who had never been out of *Leitrim*, never mind Ireland, in their lives, and I suspect he could well be right. Nobody who ever really lived in Californ-eye-ay wrote "Spancil Hill", I'm sorry.

Silence, exile and cunning, Joyce maintained, were the true weapons of the writer. But the exiles have been silent too long. And we have too frequently left cunning to the politicians who translate into platitude the part they have played in our marginalisation. Well, don't think we have gone away, those of us who have gone. When the voting rights come through, we who have so rarely spoken will be remembering the fervent promise of Coriolanus. "Long my exile, sweet my revenge."

What English newspapers call the "New Irish renaissance" in literary writing has begun to fill the exile's silence with a torrent of words. Now there are green fields all over the planet, and at last they are appearing in Irish fiction. Important and fine novels set in Spain and Germany have been published in recent years by Colm Tóibín and Hugo Hamilton. Robert McLiam Wilson and Joseph O'Neill have conjured up unique and pungent visions of London. The young short story writer Michael Collins has based himself in New York. Ronan Bennet has written about Latin America, in which troubled region Tóibín's next novel — and, indeed, my own — will be set. Meanwhile, the South London-based Galway novelist Desmond Hogan, who published first in the seventies, continues to produce some of the most evocative work in the language about places outside Ireland.

The present collection of vibrant and exciting voices is equally peripatetic. Some of these writers have been published before to enthusiastic and deserved acclaim, others receive a first outing here. But the Germany of Michael O'Loughlin, the Aranyapr - athet of Harry Clifton, the fascinatingly dis-United States of Helena Mulkerns, Aidan Hynes and Eamonn Wall, Glenn Patterson's Euro Disney, Deirdre Madden's Italy, the urban Englands of Martin Meenan, Emma Donoghue and Sara Berkeley, and the Australia of Rosita Boland are all deeply and recognisably Irish. Even the unnamed and unknown place so vividly created in Tony Keily's "Strands" is as strangely familiar as unknown places in great writing should always be. The home thoughts from abroad are just as strikingly realised, as Colum McCann sends news of Westmeath via Japan, and Colm O'Gaora imagines his birthplace of Dublin from London. Here is a generation envisioning an Ireland greater than its borders, no longer the disconnected island that it only became in the early years of its semi-independence.

Hugh MacDiarmid wrote that poets should celebrate "the drunkenness of things being various". This energetic new wave of fiction writers is claiming the right to celebrate an Ireland that is various also, in terms that are primarily aesthetic, but also, by implication, profoundly political. The silence of the Irish exile is over now. That is important.

"We are the blacks of Europe", observes a character in Roddy Doyle's novel *The Commitments*. But that isn't really true any more. Being Irish is something worth talking about, if you're on someone else's turf and lucky enough to be making enough readies to socialise occasionally with the natives. An Irish passport gives you what people in advertising call a reachier punch, I don't know why. I suspect it's more to do with U2 and Mary Robinson and Stephen Roche and Ray Houghton, than Synge, Beckett or William Trevor. People envy you these days, in New York or London or mainland Europe, if you're Irish. That's been my experience anyway. It's extraordinary. The whole world longs to be oppressed and post-colonial and tragically hip and petulantly Paddy, and we Irish just want to be *anything* else. Still, being Irish abroad — half-invader and half-native — is a fine thing for a writer to be. It means you'll probably never get shot in an airplane hijack and it certainly helps you to understand just how very Irish you are. Indeed, it sometimes seems to me that you almost have to get out of Ireland to be Irish at all, in some important sense, that those who stay turn out to be the real exiles, and those who go are the natives. But for a writer, that's material. So no complaints.

The pieces in this book give urgent voice to the new diaspora, revealing with consummate skill, consistent intelligence and, often, great humour, as many different Irelands as there are shades of green. There is a facility with language and a respect for the sheer craft of tale-telling at work here, as these stories, so various in tone, celebrate the wonder and the wandering that brings us all back home in the end. And there's very little anger. Hardly any, in fact. Just maybe, from time to time, and between the lines, we hear the faint and mordant lament of the Young Europeans on that glossy poster in Dublin airport, who have spread the grey wing, as Yeats said of the Wild Geese, and gone about the world like wind.

Wish you were here. Wish we were there. Well, sometimes anyway.

Joseph O'Connor,
London,
July 1993.

Harry Clifton

Where We Live

Where we live no longer matters
If it ever did, the difference
Between North and East, South and West,
Belfast Central, or Budapest,
Currency changed, like innocence,
For the life that was going to be ours.

Let us admit it. There are powers
No border can contain.
They sit with us, the uninvited guests,
Wherever our table is laid,
Accepting a second coffee,
Awaiting the end of the story.

They were in ourselves
From the beginning. Dark and placeless,
Asian suns, or the greys of Ulster,
Meant nothing to them. Your skies, my skies,
Everywhere in between
Was a place they could work unseen.

Here, they can rest a while
In our latest exile. Groundless,
Taking root everywhere,
Living on thin Italian air,
Our house is their house,
With the bats and the swallows,

Demons and angels, ghosting
The warm red sandstone
Of borrowed quarters. Leave us alone!
Wherever life is an open question
They have beaten us to it
Already, come into their own.

They are the lightnings
That transfigure us our troubles —
Homeless, the ancient weather
That travels inside us
And breaks out, here and there,
The days we despair of each other.

Colum McCann

Fishing
The
Sloe-Black River

The women fished for their sons in the sloe-black river that ran through the small Westmeath town, while the fathers played football in a field half a mile away. Low shouts drifted like lazy swallows over the river, interrupting the silence of the women. They were casting with ferocious hope, twenty-six of them in unison, in a straight line along the muddy side of the low-slung river wall, whipping back the rods over their shoulders. They had pieces of fresh bread mashed onto hooks so that when they cast their lines the bread volleyed out over the river and hung for a moment, making curious shapes in the air — cartwheels and tumbles and plunges. The bread landed with a soft splash on the water, and the ripples met each other gently.

The *aurora borealis* was beginning to finger the sky with light the colour of skin, wine bottles and the amber of the town's football jerseys. Drowsy clouds drifted, catching the colours from the North. A collie dog slept in the doorway of the only pub. The main street tumbled with litter.

The women along the wall stood yards apart, giving each other room so that their lines wouldn't tangle. Mrs Conheeny wore a headscarf patterned with corgi dogs, the little animals yelping at the side of her ashy hair. She had dollops of dough still stuck under her fingernails. There were splashes of mud on her wellingtons. She bent her back into the familiar work of reeling in the empty line. Each time she cast she curled her upper lip, scrunching up the crevices around her cheeks. She was wondering how Father Marsh, the old priest for whom she did the housekeeping, was doing as goalkeeper. The joke around town was that he was only good for saving souls. As she spun a little line out from the reel she worried that her husband, at right half-back, might be feeling the ache in his knee from ligaments torn long ago.

Leaning up against the river wall, tall and bosom-burdened, she sighed and whisked her fishing rod through the air.

Beside her Mrs Harrington, the artist's wife, was a salmon leap of energy, thrashing the line back and forth as deftly as a fly fisherwoman, ripping crusts from her own loaves, impaling them on the big grey hook and spinning them out of the water's blackness, frantically tapping her feet up and down on the muddy bank. Mrs Harrington's husband had been shoved in at left full-forward in the hope that he might poke a stray shot away in a goalmouth frenzy. But by all accounts — or so Mr Conheeny said — the watercolour man wasn't worth a barman's fart on the football field. Then again, they all laughed, at least he has a warm body. He could fill a position against the other teams in the county, all of whom still managed to gallop, here and there, with young bones.

Mrs Conheeny scratched at her forehead. Not a bite, not a bit, not a brat around, she thought as she reeled in her line and watched a blue chocolate wrapper get caught in a gust of wind, then float down onto the water.

The collie left the door of the pub, ambling down along the main street, by the row of townhouses, nosing in the litter outside the newsagents. Heavy roars keened through the air as the evening stole shapes. Each time the women heard the whistle blow they raised their heads in the hope that the match was finished so they could unsnap the rods and bend towards home with their picnic baskets.

Mrs Conheeny watched Mrs Hynes across the river, her face plastered with make-up, tentatively clawing at a reel. Mrs King was there with her graphite rod. Mrs McDaid had come up with the idea of putting currants in her bread. Mrs O'Shaughnessy was whipping away with a long slender piece of bamboo — did she think she was fishing in the Mississippi? Mrs Bergen, her face scrunched in pain from arthritis, was hoping her fingers might move a little better, like they used to on the antique accordion. Mrs Kelly was sipping from her little silver flask of the finest Jameson's. Mrs Hogan was casting with firefly-flicks of the wrist. Mrs Docherty was hauling in her line, as if gathering folds in her dress. And Mrs Hennessy was gently peeling the crust from a slice of Brennan's.

Further down along the pebbledashed wall Mrs McCarton was gently humming a bit of a song. "Flow on lovely river flow gently along, by your waters so clear sounds the lark's merry song." Her husband captained the team, a barrel of a man who, when he was young, consistently scored a hat trick. But the team hadn't won a game in two years, ever since the children had begun their drift.

They waited, the women, and they cast, all of them together.

When the long whistle finally cut through the air and the colours took on forms that flung themselves against the northern sky, the women slowly unsnapped their rods and placed the hooks in the lowest eyes of their rods. They looked at each other and nodded sadly. Another useless day fishing. Opening picnic baskets and lunch boxes, they put the bread away and waited for the line of Ford Cortinas and Vauxhalls and Opel Kaddets and even Mr Hogan's blue tractor to trundle down and pick them up.

Their husbands arrived with their amber jerseys splattered with mud, their faces long in another defeat, cursing under taggles of pipes, their old bones creaking at the joints.

Mrs Conheeny readjusted her scarf and watched for her husband's car. She saw him lean over and ritually open the door even before he stopped. She ducked her head to get in, put the rod and basket in the back seat. She waved to the women who were still waiting, then took off her headscarf.

"Any luck, love?" he asked.

She shook her head:"I didn't even get a bite."

She looked out to the sloe-black river as they drove off, then sighed. One day she would tell him how useless it all was, this fishing for sons, when the river looked not a bit like the Thames or the Darling or the Hudson or the Loire or even the Rhine itself, where their own three sons were working in a car factory. But he slapped his hands on the steering wheel and said with a sad laugh: "Well fuck it all anyway, we need some new blood in midfield," though she knew that he too would go fishing that night, silently slipping out, down to the river, to cast in vain.

Michael O'Loughlin

Traditional Music

The first day we walked into that factory in Germany, and they handed us our work clothes — green boots, white overalls and orange gloves — we all cracked up. They were tailor-made for us. But of course, they weren't — they had just been waiting for us to fill them. Anyway, the hilarity didn't last. The work in the factory was boring and sometimes exhausting, the German foremen were authoritarian and rude. Soon, we were devoting most of our energy to devising ways of tormenting them, such as roaring out choruses of the Horst Wessel, to the great amusement of the Turks who formed the majority of the work force. Anyway, we were students and none of it was quite real.

We had come with the intention of earning some money, and while we were at it, getting a good look at the fabled continent. For many of us it was the first time ever abroad, not counting England or America. After we had got over the first flush of bars that didn't close, and the beauty of the local girls, we quickly reverted to what we really liked doing: sitting around, arguing about politics with our friends. Exhausted by the day's work, we tended to stay close to the hostel where we were lodged, hanging out in the bar around the corner, which had a great table football game. Sometimes, we would trek across town to The Purple Windmill, where the town's dope dealers held court and there was a kind of "scene".

One night, however, bad-tempered nostalgia drew us to The Irish Rover. As a rule, we tended to avoid it, with its Irish Tourist Board posters of currachs and Georgian Doors, Guinness on tap and the Dubliners on tape. It was usually full of off-duty American soldiers, local would-be IRA sympathizers, and Englishmen from Stoke or Newcastle shouting around the dart board in incomprehensible accents. This night we were sitting there at the bar, contemptuously drinking bad Guinness, when Ciaran attached himself to us.

He heard us talking and walked over, proclaiming:

"You're Irish, aincha? So am I." This was in an outrageous Cockney accent, the kind that tends towards falsetto.

We found Ciaran very amusing. He was a big-boned, swarthy fellow, as English as the Old Kent Road. Football, darts and tarts, Coronation Street and pints of bitter, that was Ciaran. His parents, however, were native Irish speakers from the wilds of Connemara. His sister played the accordion in a Céilí Band. All of this he communicated to us with great rapidity, as he ordered a drink. He had been playing darts with some English workmates who now called him to take his place. He waved them away impatiently. We made room for him at the bar.

There was something touching about his much professed Irishness, and he kept us amused with his endless supply of stories about the East End of small-time criminals, professional boxers and afternoon drinking clubs, this being the milieu he had grown up in, and which we found fascinating. I had an image of him as a child, for some reason, fighting and cursing on the narrow streets near the docks, and then stepping into the little house, where his parents stared at him as if he were a stranger, murmuring to each other in Irish. But now that he was getting a little older, he had rediscovered himself. He was overcome with enthusiasm at finding us. Later that night, he said:

"Listen, you've got to meet a cunt I know. She loves the Irish. Buys horses in Ireland you know." We laughed.

"What's she do?" asked Baxter. "Is she a butcher?"

But Ciaran was all earnestness.

"No, listen. She is a cunt, know what I mean? A fucking cunt, grade A. Like, it's not a love job or anything like that. I met her in 'ere a few weeks ago. I'll bring her here on Friday night so you can meet her. Real German bitch she is."

By the time the Irish Rover closed, we were quite drunk, and resolved to go to a local disco. We walked into a large space filled with coloured lights. The deafening music was some piece of pop with high girlish choruses, and machine-like monotonous rhythm characteristic of continental pop — what they call the Eurothump. On one side, in Hawaiian shirts, were the Americans, the whites like bloated albinos, the blacks undernourished and nervous. On the other side, were hordes of nubile teenagers in T-shirts and jeans.

"Welcome to Downtown Europe," was Baxter's comment. It was virtually impossible to talk with the noise. Eventually, predictably, a nasty fight erupted between some Americans and some of the local young people. We gathered that this was a regular occurrence. We decided that we had had enough of European nightlife, and left.

When we walked into the Irish Rover on Friday night, Ciaran was there with the girl.

"Hey mates! This is Renate."

We all said hello and nodded, with little ambiguous Irish smiles.

Renate was a solidly built blonde in jeans, not tall for a German. She was good-looking, but her jaw was just a bit too heavy for her to be called really beautiful. Her hair, longish and a bit thin, was pushed back from her heavy-set face, which had an almost angelic expression, the eyes candid.

"You're Irish," she asked, making it sound as if it was a status, like being a film star. We could only concur.

"I love Ireland very much, you know" she said. I noticed that as she talked, she looked at you very intently, as if she was reading something written on the inside of the back of your skull.

"Ciaran told me that you breed horses."

"No, not exactly. I import Irish horses to Germany, and sell them here. But I plan in the next couple of years to buy a farm there and do something with horses myself."

"Proper little Lady Fucking Chatterly, eh?!" said Ciaran, laughing.

She looked at him with not quite hatred, more a cool calculation of revenge deferred. She reached out and stroked his chest. They glared at each other like cats.

"We'll all come and work for you then," I said.

"Well yes, that would be nice." She laughed. "What I'm really planning to do is buy a nice farm with a big house, and I'll bring people over from Germany for horse-riding holidays. I think it can be a big success. I have just seen a nice place in Galway, near the ocean."

"Pity about the people though," said Baxter.

"What? Which people?" said Renate, genuinely puzzled.

"Forget it," said Baxter, "Would you like a drink?"

Ciaran had sat there contentedly, looking from us to Renate, and back again. Now he interjected: "Hey listen, have you 'eard about the Irish Folk Festival tomorrow?"

"No, what's all that about?"

"There's a big festival... look..." He rummaged around in his pocket and came up with a flyer printed in lurid green ink, headed: *Monster Irish Folk Festival!* It seemed there was to be a one-day festival in the nearby city tomorrow. This was the era when a part of European youth had been obsessed by Irish traditional music. It literally saved a whole generation from destitution. Hordes of long-haired, mustachioed young men with the ability to knock a tune out of a banjo or tin whistle foraged up and down the motorways of Europe playing to crowds bigger than the population of their native villages. Between times they would go back to Ireland to sit around in bars, with exotic labels on their instrument cases and sometime a blonde girl in tow. Now, it was at its peak. A promoter had chartered a jet for the weekend, flown to Dublin, and loaded it up with traditional musicians. With his plane full he flew back to Germany. It looked like it might be good fun.

"Yeah, let's go."

We drank more and grew enthusiastic. We agreed to all go together, myself, Baxter, Ciaran and Renate in Renate's car.

She picked us up the next morning. We were all in good form, light-headed with hangovers from the night before. Renate looked great, in jeans and a white shirt, and silver boots. We joined the autobahn just outside the town. We chatted away, having fun. Eventually she said she wanted to stop. We pulled into a picnic area, and opened some tins of beer. I left the others and walked a little way into the forest. It was very quiet in there, and very foreign. That is, it made me suddenly feel very foreign, someone who didn't belong here. For some reason, a couple of lines of poetry I must have learnt in school, by Yeats I think, came into my mind:

Who will go drive with Fergus now
And pierce the deep wood's woven shade.

Who indeed? I was slightly hungover and now I felt shivery with a sudden attack of neurotic anxiety. I shook it off. There was a great day ahead of us. I walked back to the picnic area.

Back on the autobahn, we sped toward the city. We left the autobahn just outside it. The place where the festival was to be held was out on the outskirts, though once it had been a centre, an enormous train station, the hub of a great wheel of empire. Now it was beached, I thought grandiloquently, by the tides of history, a broken stump, like the little country lanes you sometimes find surrounded by concrete in the suburbs of Dublin. No trains came near it anymore, it was used for concerts and exhibitions. There had just been a huge exhibition of modern Bulgarian art. And today it was hosting the Monster Irish Folk Festival.

When we got there it was already filling up, there was an air of anticipation and excitement. Seasoned German festival-goers carried car seats into the hall, litres of water, children. A van pulled up and a dozen or so men spilled out, unmistakably Irish in their demeanour and colouring.

"Ah," said Baxter, "the currachs have landed."

We paid our money and had a green harp stamped on the back of our hands as token of entry. As we walked in we saw, suspended behind the stage, the biggest tricolour I had ever seen. Laughing, we headed straight for the bar and bought beer. The sun streamed in from the huge glass roof. And then the music started.

Sometimes it was a slim girl singing unaccompanied in Irish, her voice strangely distorted by the massive banks of speakers on either side of the stage. Sometimes it was one of the dynamic, skilful young ensembles like Clannad, or the Bothy Band. We stood in a clump near the stage, drinking and talking. Ciaran was having the time of his life.

"Fucking magic, innit?" he said. Renate grinned beside him. I noticed that a distant cousin of mine was playing in one of the bands. I went backstage to chat with him.

"Jaysus, howa Pat. How's it goin? What the fuck are you doing here?"

"I could ask you the same question."

He laughed: "It's better than working anyway." He rolled up a joint and we smoked it, chatting with a group of musicians sitting around. They were talking about an incident which had happened the night before. One of the most distinguished members of the entourage was an old fiddler from Kerry famous the world over for the purity of his style, the uniqueness of his repertoire. Last night there had been a big session in the hotel where they were all staying, which had inevitably attracted a few fans. One of them, a young girl, had been fascinated by the old man who filled the spaces between tunes with his strange poetic maundering. She arranged to go up to his room later and record some of his monologues for posterity. When she knocked on his door, he had opened it and stood before her in all his ancient nakedness, except for his cap and boots. They had heard her screams all over the hotel.

On top of the beer, the dope was hitting me the wrong way. I felt depressed. I wandered back out to the hall, where the old fiddler was playing. A television camera was being held a couple of feet away from his face. Behind him, somebody with a hand-held camera was filming him and the TV filming him. I looked out at the crowd, so many fresh young faces looking up appreciatively, curiously, their little harps stamped on their hands. What were they hearing and seeing? I headed hungrily for the bar, where the Irish were congregated, growing ever more animated. Some of them were dancing. This was very funny, as like most Irish people they didn't know how to. They hopped in the air, alternately kicking their legs. Some Germans were reverently imitating them.

The music went on relentlessly, like a train that couldn't be stopped.

Towards the end of the afternoon, I fell asleep. I dreamt I was in a huge train station, totally deserted. It was night and winter, and the tracks stretched out into a mist. High above me, the air was full of screaming metallic sounds. How had I gotten here? The trains had all arrived and left a long time ago. I was alone. Then I heard, somewhere far off in the distance, a tin whistle playing some melancholy tune. I tried to find it. I travelled down damp tunnels and dirty stairs and from one platform to the next, but I couldn't find where the music was coming from. I was getting cold. I woke with a start. I was lying on the concrete. Of course, there was a girl on the stage playing a tin whistle.

There was a kind of hiatus now, before the real evening began. Everybody was tired, we had all drunk so much that we had reached a plateau of sobriety. But of course, this was deceptive. We kept drinking, and like a car changing gear, things began to speed up, the momentum of the alcohol and music pushing us faster and faster. The music, though, was getting tedious. The serious bands had all finished. Now there were mainly old ballad groups singing cabaret chestnuts and republican ballads. We were losing interest. A group of about twenty or thirty Irishmen had congregated near the stage, around a little cairn of beer tins. Things seemed to reach a manic stage, get blurred. It was only after that I was able to put them in their proper sequence. The last group came on, and we tried to drown them out with our roared parodies of Irish songs:

"They hated old Ireland
and they ran from all danger
Glory O Glory O
to the bold Emig-rant!"

31

But we had more or less lost interest by then, and ignored the national anthem. A bearded man came on and made an impassioned speech in German about the sufferings of the Irish people. We grew silent and sullen. He demanded that we contribute to the waging of the people's liberation struggle. The huge crowd around us cheered and stamped their feet. Then it started. The Irish began reaching into the pile of beer cans and flinging them at the man on the stage. I felt a sudden dislocation. I was reeling. I slowly realised that somebody had punched me in the face. It was all shouting and confusion. I wandered away, dazed, and leaned against a metal rail. Renate was holding my head.

"Are you alright?" She looked frightened, or rather, surprised. Her easy casualness was gone.

I was alright. I stood up. Ciaran was walking towards us, his face a mask of fury and outrage. There was blood on his white jeans.

"Cunt! The fucking cunts stabbed me!" He was so full of righteous indignation, I almost laughed. Renate knelt down and examined the wound at the top of his thigh.

"It doesn't seem to me too bad, it's just a cut. But maybe you should go to the hospital anyway and get a stitch."

"Fuck off" said Ciaran without looking at her.

Somehow the crowd had vanished. The hall was now empty, except for the bulldozer-like machines clearing up the beer cans and papers, the technicians dismantling the speakers and the small knot of Irishmen in the ruins of the bar, deep in disputation. I saw Baxter sitting on the cairn, thoughtfully drinking a can of beer. Sitting beside him, in a state of great upset, was the man, or rather boy, who had stabbed Ciaran with his Swiss Army penknife. He was German, and had thought that Ciaran was an Englishman. Ciaran was so incensed by this we couldn't help laughing. The four of us went out to the car and headed for a hospital. Renate was agitated.

"But why did you all do that? Why? I just don't understand."

"It's very simple really, Renate," said Baxter. "Y'see..."

But I didn't listen. I knew the explanation as well as he did, but somehow, I knew that no matter how you explained it, I would still feel unclean, disgusted with the whole thing.

The casualty unit was crowded, and we had to wait for a while, sitting in the harsh hospital light. Baxter had salvaged a six-pack, and we drank it.

"Look at the bright side, Ciaran. You'll probably be able to apply to the Irish Government for a pension. You're a wounded veteran of the Irish Civil War," said Baxter.

We went over the events of the day again and again, polishing up the highlights, turning them into anecdotes we would tell each other someday about our uproarious spalpeen youth. I noticed that Renate had left us and was talking to a tall young doctor on the other side of the room. He offered her a cigarette. With a start, I realised they were speaking German. I had never heard her speak it before. Of course, she was German, so there was nothing strange about that. Why did it surprise me? I listened. By now, I had picked up a few words of the language. I heard the doctor, with a flick of his head in our direction, ask her who we were. She glanced towards us, and said something, the only word I could pick out was one I knew: *Ausländer*. For a second, I didn't realise she was talking about us. Christ! I suddenly saw the three of us as she and her smooth doctor must see us, sitting there huddled on a bench with our beer and bloodstains, and our anecdotes. That was what we were to her: *Ausländer*. This year the Irish, the next year who knows? South America? We were just holograms, images passing across her eyes. But was she anything more than that to us? What was it in her that drove her to us, out of her natural environment? What was she looking for?

I felt dizzy. I stood up and walked to the window that looked out on the car park. I looked back at Ciaran and Baxter sitting on the bench, still chatting away. I remembered the day I had first seen Sean Baxter, the day we had started our lives as men. We had sat nervously in the strange classroom, as Father Daly had distributed the little black books. He then opened one and read the first sentence, with solemnity, making us all aware of the importance of this moment: *Omnia Gallia in partes tres divisa est...*

The doctor called Ciaran in, and gave him a stitch. Within minutes we were back out in the car park, getting into Renate's car. She had recovered her mood, but the rest of us were now subdued, hungover. The day was over, the day we went to the festival, the day Ciaran got stabbed. Now we were just waiting for it to finish. Ciaran ostentatiously got into the back, so I sat in the front. We drove out through the suburbs and onto the autobahn. It was empty, a grey plane stretching out ahead of us and behind us. Renate drove fast, intently, speeding towards her Ireland, the road unfolding its scenario in front of her.

I looked back at the two behind me. They were lying back, eyes blank, looking out the window. I turned back. I had the sensation I had been here before. I thought of Caesar again, and how I had loved that book. I had read it dozens of times, translated it, underlined it, construed it. But love was the wrong word: from the beginning it had fascinated and frustrated me. The Latin was like a brick wall, that forced me to fling myself at it again and again. And even when I had mastered the grammar, knew every word, the wall was still there, and I had to get at whatever it was that was behind it. Now, strapped into a car speeding through the night, on the empty autobahn, I felt a black hole opening up in my mind, and I was falling through it. I saw what I, unbeknownst to myself, had been looking for. As Caesar had marched north, we had marched with him, with his laws, his grammar, his plumbing, his Greeks. And while we were marching with him, we were crouched down in our forests, in our earthen forts, with our idols, our severed heads, our bubbling language, waiting for him. We were both Caesar and Vercingetorix. Which is to say we were nothing, nowhere: *Ausländer...*

Beside me, Renate was humming some strange translation of an Irish tune under her breath. Suddenly she slapped my leg with her right hand:

"Hey! Irish! Why aren't you singing? I thought you Irish were always singing."

Glenn Patterson

from

Black Night
at
Big Thunder Mountain

" These are the words of the Lord of Hosts, the God of
Israel: to all the exiles whom I deported from
Jerusalem to Babylon. Build houses and live in
them, plant gardens and eat the produce; marry
wives and rear families; choose wives for your sons
and give your daughters to husbands, so that they
may bear sons and daughters."

At seven twenty-five that morning, local time, a minibus was
motoring, in light entirely of its own creation, along a country
road in Marne-la-Vallee, east of Paris, radio tuned to the morning
prayer from London.

" Increase there and do not dwindle away. Seek the
welfare of any city to which I have exiled you and do
not dwindle away. Seek the welfare of any city to
which I have exiled you, and pray to the Lord for it;
on its welfare, your welfare will depend."

In the minibus are sixteen Northern Irish labourers and
tradesmen travelling into work from their digs in a converted
monastery south of Crecy-la-Chapelle. Two men sit up front with
the driver, the remainder are packed in the back in unequal rows
of six and seven, the spare man, jammed between his neighbour
and the door, more out of his seat than in.

There are few houses to be seen. On either side the road falls away unbordered into dark flat fields. Sleet flurries dash against the windscreen like swarms of night insects. It is cold in the bus and black and silent. The men hug themselves for warmth. Only the driver appears to be fully awake.

> "These are the words of the Lord: When a full 70 years have passed over Babylon, I shall take up your cause and make good my promise to bring you back to this place. I alone know my purpose for you, says the Lord: wellbeing and not misfortune, and a long line of descendants after you."

A wan stripe appears unpromisingly along the horizon to the east. The driver lights a cigarette from the element in the dashboard. The man behind him coughs, without waking, the man beside him shifts his weight on to the other hip. The momentum continues along the uneven line, increasing in magnitude as it passes, so that the sixth man's giant sigh dislodges the seventh man altogether and tips him on his arse on the floor. The seventh man doesn't even try to get up. Consciousness forms, a thin ice between him and the depths of sleep. He tells himself he's as well off where he is. His name is Raymond Black, he has only recently been moved to the Monastery from Fulbanes and he isn't one to start a fuss. From the floor he sees twelve pairs of folded arms, twelve heads lolling over twelve shadowy chests. He sees roadside poplars ignite for a moment in the minibus's headlights, then turn to instant silver skeletons in its wake. After a few moments he lets his own head fall forward again, folding in on himself, back through the ice, dragging the shards of World Service news beneath the surface with him.

Vukovar. A word like the crack and echo of a single rifleshot, drifting through smoke from which a building slowly emerges: a warehouse? yes, on the edge of a nameless Russian city. Inside, he knows, are six Red Army soldiers. They have held up the German advance for two days with only their rifleshots. The world is at war and Raymond Black is the narrator. He forms a sentence incorporating the words courage and terror. His voice is coming from inside the warehouse itself: a message, a mayday, an act of defiance. And then the transmission cuts out and he wakes.

The minibus is parked in a filling station forecourt, its engine and radio both silent. Instead a transistor is playing in the station shop. The reception is poor, swooping and soaring, from wavelength to wavelength, from speech to song, mixing the two into screech and babble. Ecstatic.

Vukovar. Raymond remembers at children's church in Belfast how he sang and clapped and shouted and the walls of Jericho came tumbling down. (He tries to remember Jericho's crime, but can't.) He remembers later at school, on a page in his history book headed the Last Days of Rome, a picture of a Vandal tugging an old man's beard and the shame he felt every time he read the terse inscription *Rome fell and was sacked.*

The driver gets back into the cab and finishes the docked cigarette from a sundae dish of butts blutacked to the dashboard. The bus lurches out on to the road. The men lurch with it. There is a rumour doing the rounds that they are all going to be put on a month's notice at the end of the week. There have been no new starts for going on a fortnight as it is and some of the other contractors are already paying off their skilled men. It'll be all over by Christmas is the new catchphrase.

Raymond uses the new door handle to pull himself up level with the window. Houses begin to appear with some regularity now at the side of the road; they clot into villages, the villages in turn into a small town. None makes any lasting impression on the darkness. But then at a certain point beyond the town the road dips for a moment and bends and when it rises again the sky has erupted into colour a mile or so distant. Lights stretch back as far as the eye can see, running off to the left and the right, clambering up the sides of buildings, silhouetting turrets and mountain peaks. The minibus finds itself in a flow of traffic which thickens and slows as more traffic joins at each new junction. Across the unveiled fields other roads can now be made out drawing still more traffic in towards the centre. Buses, vans, lorries, taxis, private cars, motorbikes and pushbikes; and everywhere, from nowhere, groups of men, few of them white, walking. Hands slap on the side of the minibus, faces appear at the sleety windows mouthing words for lift. *Away and fuck!* the driver says and holds the horn down with his fist. The men inside begin to come awake. They light cigarettes, look out over their shoulders at the acres of carparks they pass alongside, at the builders' compounds with their national flags and own-language signs — little Italies and Belgiums and two kinds of Irelands — or squint through the wipers at the pink and blue castle and the stiff red fingers of Big Thunder Mountain.

"Are we past the Queen's Bridge yet?" some joker asks and the men smile remembering other mornings closer to home. Raymond smiles too.

The joker stops joking and leans forward.

"What are you smirking at, Black?" he says and twelve pairs of eyes all turn on Raymond, as the sleet turns to rain — as Vukovar falls — as the Euro Disney rush hour peaks and the minibus is waved through the gate and is lost among the lights and the mud and the clamour and the roar.

Deirdre Madden

From

Remembering Light & Stone

In 1989, when the Berlin Wall is coming down, Ashling — the Irish narrator — has been living for four years in an Italian village, coming to terms with her Irish childhood and the death of her parents. This is the novel's opening chapter.

"I don't belong here." The thought came to me with such force that I almost said it aloud, at once, but I stopped myself just in time. I know what he would have said, reasonably: "Do I?"

Later, looking back on that last day in Rome, what I would remember would be the heat and the noise. It was a struggle to be in the city because of that, but there was a curious softness too. The violent heat released the scent of fruit from the stalls as we walked past: melons, peaches, nectarines, plums. The fruit and vegetables were stacked outside the little shops in frail wooden crates. Near Campo Dei Fiori there was a woman who tended a stall, and she was singing as she brushed the city dust from the fruit with a spray of coloured feathers. It was the longest day of the year.

Ted wanted a drink, so we sat down at a table outside a café. We didn't say much to each other as we sat there, but watched the people drift along the hot street in their gaudy summer clothes and heavy jewellery. After a while Ted said to me that, for him, there was always a strong sense of death in the south, because of the very emphasis on life. The sun itself that made the fruit so ripe and big, that seemed to make the people bloom so early and so evidently, mercilessly pushed everything over into decay, so that the fruit quickly rotted, and the people suddenly fell into a graceless old age.

I thought of Franca's daughter, Lucia. She was fifteen, almost a woman and completely at ease with the fact, but I could see what Ted meant. I could see the short duration of that ease, and how there was something frail and uncertain about her whole self, as though she might at any moment topple headlong into being an old woman in a black dress, with nothing to look forward to but death. Time and again I remembered looking into the faces of young women in Italy, and seeing peer back, unbeknownst to them, the faces of the women they would be some fifty years later.

So I understood what Ted meant, and in a way I agreed with him, but I wasn't completely convinced, because I didn't want to be. I associated the north with violence and death, and I had come south to escape that.

Deep down, I knew that what he said was true, and that it was one of the many things people didn't understand about Italy, the people, that is, who came south to Italy, where "everybody is so happy." No one wants to shatter the myth of the warm, sensual, happy south, for if we did not believe in that, where would people go to escape the rigour of the north? I had learnt a lot about Italy in the time I had been there, but what I had learnt most of all was how little I understood it, how deceptive a country it was. And more than learning anything about Italy, I had found out more about my own country, simply by not being in it. The contrast with Italy was a help, but in many ways I felt I could have gone anywhere, so long as it was far away and provided me with privacy, so that I could forget all about home for a while, forget all about Ireland, and then remember it, undisturbed.

Once, I visited some limestone caverns up near Trieste, and it reminded me of the Burren, where I grew up. I realised then how much I loved that strange, stark beauty, the bare grey stone and the grey sky, the few stunted trees. I missed that landscape when I lived away from it, and had taken it for granted when I was there.

I looked across the table at Ted, and I thought of how I had no word to define him, or his relationship to me, and I was glad that it was so. I remembered expressions I had heard used when I was growing up, such as "going steady". I found phrases like that completely absurd, they sounded to me as quaint and outmoded as "keeping company". I hate convenient empty words, they trap you when you use them. Franca used to call him my *fidanzato*, and I didn't like that either. It was a word that smelt of matrimony, and yet it was vague, too. There was no word to describe the degree of distance and intimacy there was between us. I think I realized then that it was coming to an end, and that we wouldn't be together for much longer, but of course I didn't say anything.

The waiter brought me a little black bitter coffee, the sort I hated when I first went to Italy, but which I grew to love. The pleasure and fascination of other countries has never left me, and I hope it never does. One of my most vivid childhood memories, certainly one of the most pleasant, is of the time a Japanese woman came to visit our neighbours. Until then, I had never met a person from such a distant country, and I was completely fascinated by her. One day I went into the house where she was staying, and she was talking to someone on the phone in her own language, and I was amazed to think that for her all those sounds came so easily, she understood so much and knew so much. She gave me a coloured paper fan that smelt of smoke, and on a sheet of strange paper- pale green, with a pearly sheen to it — she wrote with black ink and a little brush the characters that stood for her name — Yuriko — and mine — Aisling. I said that some day I would go to Japan to visit her, but my brother Jimmy teased me about it. He said that I'd hate it there because I'd have to eat raw fish and seaweed. "You'll have to eat rice with your dinner, too." That seemed really odd to me, for I had only ever seen rice cooked in milk and served with prunes. He told me that I wouldn't like the tea, because it was green, and that they wouldn't let me put milk in it, I'd have to drink it black. That made me think it was all a lie, for if the tea was green, how could you drink it black? I told Jimmy I didn't believe him, told him I didn't care, and that some day I'd go away, to see other countries. My image of what those countries would be like was strange and limited, as is often the case with children. For years I thought that New York was America, that is, I thought it was all skyscrapers from coast to coast. I was shocked and disappointed when I found out there were trees and fields too. (I had once told Ted this and he had said, "Forget about kids, Aisling: I've met adults who think everywhere in America looks like Manhattan.") When Yuriko went back to Japan she sent me a postcard, showing the white cone of Mount Fuji under snow. The sky behind was deep blue, the foreground full of yellow flowers. I kept the card, in a safe place, together with the fan and the sheet of paper with our names on it. For me, they were magical things. When I grew up I did go away, but I never got to Japan. I had almost forgotten Yuriko, it was the first time I had thought of her in years. I wondered where she was now, what she was doing, and if she remembered me.

Ted interrupted my thoughts. He touched my hands, and, nodding, said quietly, "Look over there."

He indicated three small girls, shabbily dressed and barefoot, who were each holding large torn pieces of corrugated cardboard. They had approached a smartly dressed woman who was looking in a shop window and tugged her sleeve to attract her attention. At once she was surrounded. All talking at once, the children held out their hands, demanding alms, while holding the cardboard out flat to create a little shelf between themselves and the woman. She was shocked and disoriented to find herself the centre of attention, when the children suddenly scattered as quickly as they had gathered, the smallest one triumphantly waving a slim leather wallet. The woman screamed as she looked down at her handbag, which hung gaping open from her arm, having been craftily opened and swiftly rifled by little hands. It was, of course, all over in seconds: by the time the woman had started to scream and the people around her noticed what had happened, the children were out of sight.

Ted shook his head. "You wonder how they keep getting away with it. Reminds me of the first time I came to Italy. I had had all the warnings, and then two days after I arrived, down in the Forum, exactly the same thing. Three hundred dollars in lire gone in ten seconds. Losing the money was bad, going to see the Italian police was almost worse. They just said, "You're the tenth in today." You could see they'd had it with stupid *Americani*, getting mugged and then coming to them, as if there was anything they could do to get the cash back. I almost thought the kids were right, I felt kind of sorry for them, even though the little bastards cleaned me out."

The city was full of poor children, they were like the pigeons or the wild cats, to be found around all the big monuments, the Colosseum, the Forum, in the big squares and in the streets. Earlier that day, I had seen a tiny girl, without shoes, who walked up and down beside a row of cars which were stopped at traffic lights, begging at the car windows. When the lights changed, she huddled in the middle of the streams of traffic, which made no effort to avoid her, nor, I suppose, did she expect it to. When the lights were red again, she resumed her task, walking patiently from window to window. In the time I watched her, nobody gave her anything.

The preceding evening, just a few hours after we got into Rome, we had been having dinner in a restaurant. We had almost finished the meal, and were talking over coffee and fruit about what we would do the following day. The door opened, and a little girl came in, carrying an armful of red roses, each one sheathed in cellophane. She started to go from table to table, and was rebuffed at each one, the diners often barely looking up from their food to tell her to go away. As she approached our table I said to Ted, "Buy me one, please." He asked the little girl how much they cost.

"Two thousand."

Ted gave her five, and waved away the change. She put the green note in her pocket without a word, handed me a rose, and drifted off to the remaining tables. She had a deep cut above her right eye, her cheek was marked by the last shadow of a bruise, and her whole face showed utter exhaustion. Disappointment and bitterness were stamped upon her features in a way that would have been shocking to see in a woman of forty. She had had enough, and her face expressed the unconscious question: "If this is life, why was I ever born?" She must have been barely six years old. To show her pity would have been to torment her. The child had reached the door again, and she went out into the night.

I recognized the child. Seeing her made me want to withdraw, and I felt a terrible sense of despair. Some years earlier, I had read an article in a newspaper about child pornography. It was a short article, which described how many children were sold into slavery, how films and photographs were found, showing little children crying, being raped and beaten and cut, showing childlen being killed. When I read that, it was as if something had fallen over me. Suddenly everything changed, my fingernails on the edge of the newspaper looked different, the sun on the wall, the feel of my feet in my shoes; everything, everything. I wanted all at once not to be a part of a world where such things could happen. I felt guilty, as though simply by being in such a society, I was acquiescing to its evils. I wanted to do something to show that I was turning away irrevocably from such things, that I could not, would not tolerate them.

All this was brought back to me by the sight of the little girls who stole the woman's wallet. My face must have been as dark as my mind while this chain of thoughts absorbed me, for I realized that Ted was looking at me anxiously. He didn't understand, because he said to me, "Don't worry, Aisling. You'll be all right when we get there." For a moment, I didn't know what he was talking about, and then I remembered where we were going the following day. "It's not that at all," I told him. "I am looking forward to going back, although I am a bit nervous too." He didn't ask me what I had been thinking about, and I was grateful for that.

I'll probably never know what brought Ted and me together, nor what then kept us together for that time. I don't think it matters, I think it's best that it remain a mystery, even to me, or perhaps particularly to me. I don't believe in trying to analyse things like that. I know he was very fond of me, but he was afraid of me too. At first he used to deny it, but then he admitted it. I knew in Rome that it was getting to the point where he was more frightened than fond, and so it probably wouldn't last much longer. It was too hot to move. I wanted to go on sitting there at the café table. A short distance away, beyond the pavement, the phenomenal traffic of Rome roared past. I was glad I didn't live in Rome, I didn't think I could ever become used to it. It wasn't the idea of living in a big city that put me off, because I had once lived in Paris. In Rome it was a combination of things — the disorganization, — the hellish heat, the constant traffic. I remembered how it had shocked me when I had first arrived there, and even after having lived in Italy for years, I could still evoke from it that feeling of strangeness. It can feel as if I'm looking at everything backwards, down a long tunnel of time.

I remembered standing one day, waiting to cross the road in Rome. I could smell the dust and pollution and could hardly bear the terrible heat which was coming off the vehicles and beating down like a hammer from the sun; the sun was like bronze. Every so often the traffic would stop, snarled up on itself. Suddenly this happened and I found I was looking into the face of a man driving a big white Landrover. And it was the strangest thing, because I felt that I was looking at a person from an ancient civilization. I saw the whole scene in terms of both time and space, and I saw its absurdity, for there was so much traffic and the jeep in particular was so stupidly big that I knew at once it was all bound to end. It was a completely transient phenomenon, it had only existed for forty years, at most, out of the thousands and millions of years during which there had been life. It was all an aberration, and it was doomed. All the big roads made for it would one day be empty. I looked intently at the man behind the wheel. He looked as innocent as a dead warrior. In his face there was not a trace of doubt, not a hint of the frailty of his own life, his times, his transport. It seemed extraordinary to me that in this city above all, with the evidence all around of broken monuments and vainglorious ruins, people seemed unaware of what would happen. Maybe one of the hardest things is to see beyond your own society, to step out of the collective consciousness of your time, but it teaches you about things as nothing else does. You begin to see your own age not with understanding, perhaps, but with compassion. You see the weakness and smallness of things which are now great or powerful. Sights which might at other times have filled me with contempt now moved me to pity, such as the overdressed women with their jewels and their expensive clothes in the *Caffe Greco*, the pity you might feel for bones found in an ancient tomb, a priceless ring on each fingerbone. I pity them their deaths in a way that they do not pity themselves, and I pity them for their faith in frail mortal things, for not knowing that there will be nothing left but weeds and broken stones.

That afternoon, Ted and I had been to see the frescoes in the Sistine Chapel. They had only been opened to the public again earlier that spring following restoration. Ted had seen them since then, but I hadn't. Looking at them it was easy to believe that they would last for such a long time, but they wouldn't last for ever. No matter how magnificent they are, paintings are made of paint, wood, canvas, clay, and no matter how well they are preserved or restored decay is built into them. Afterwards, because we were so near it, we visited St Peter's. I hadn't been there for years, mainly because I don't like it. As soon as we went in, I could see why. It frightens me. Worse, I feel that I'm supposed to be frightened, that the whole building has been carefully planned to that very end. Usually, I like churches and cathedrals. When I was living in Paris, I used to go to Notre-Dame and the Ste Chapelle quite often, especially in winter. What I was talking about earlier — the facility for stepping out of your own age — is something that these churches lend themselves to well. You can feel a sensibility, a belief in an order which has gone now, but which people long for still, and they visit those churches for exactly that. But sometimes people visit such places because they feel they ought to, because the guidebook tells them to go there. As we walked around St Peter's, I looked at all the other people and I wondered if they liked it, and if so, did they only like it because they felt they should? I suppose all that heavy gilt and marble may appeal to some people. It frightened me. We walked across the wide, empty floors, and looked up at the monstrous, mosaiced cupola. It was too big, and out of proportion. A gothic cathedral, whatever its size, can calm your spirit, and in nature too, a massive tree, a mountain or the ocean itself can have the same effect. I felt, in St Peter's, the terror you sometimes feel in a completely empty landscape.

And perhaps the most foolish thing of all was that I believed I should identify with it. Like the people who felt they ought to admire it, I thought I ought to feel some sort of affinity, because it was "my" church. I'm still prone to notions like this. I am not a free person. To know it is small consolation.

Nobody was praying. Instead, they were milling about, taking photographs and consulting guidebooks in a variety of languages, and then I noticed a small side chapel, reserved for prayer. I thought of Franca, and I asked Ted to wait for a moment while I went in to pray for her.

On the altar, there was a large gold monstrance, with a host in it, and in front of it, kneeling in an attitude of prayer were two nuns. They were both wearing long blue veils which almost covered them completely, veils which reached the floor with cloth to spare. I couldn't pray: I could hardly contain my anger at seeing those veils, at the crass cynical theatre of it. But then I thought of Franca: she would probably have liked it, been quite impressed by the sight. I think Ted was surprised at how quickly I reappeared.

On that last night in Rome, I couldn't sleep, because of the heat, and because I kept thinking of where we were going the following day, and I was thinking of the churches, all the churches I knew. Some of them still meant a great deal to me, those medieval churches where the raw power of Christianity could speak to me from the anguished face of a painted angel, over the roar of the traffic, in the heat of the night, as I lay there wrapped in a sheet, feeling the pulse of my own heart, and hearing the voice of a tormented angel scream down through the centuries to me.

Tony Keily

Strands

The girl had never enjoyed what's known as a childhood. Nor anything else as far as anyone could see. She walked with her face down, chewing at her slack lips. She was overworked and underfed, and her fingers were long and raw. Her father beat her on a routine basis, but without a strict programme. Under her grey clothing long brown and purple welts ran over smooth yellowish skin. These bruises were the only colourful thing about her, and normally they stayed hidden.

Her father was a big formless man. He stank of shit and had a red lumpy face whose mouth was never still. He chewed with his broken teeth on the awful fact that he wasn't happy. His shouting was terrible when he drank from unlabelled bottles of spirit distilled from potato, corn, who knows, maybe even straw or detritus. Of course he dressed in thick tweeds that were of course never changed. Eating was important for him. She could see him horsing in her mind's eye, cheeks bursting. Streams of stew-juice dribbled from the twitching mouth corners. Continuous shovelling of the coarse food she prepared mechanically. Her hands peeled and chopped in pails of brown-stained water filled from the freezing gush of the iron pump in the yard. She gazes out of the window, yawns, hopes he won't find a fragment of bone in his swill.

A buttery sun sinks into wet dreary hills: completely depressing scenery that's all the more depressing because it's so typical. Surely this place can't be her home? Yes, it can. She's lived for a long time in an outhouse. The father has good reason for this. There's no mother and he knows the dangers as she grows older. This separation has never been explained to her. She was kicked out of the main house at the age of eight. As she grew up she sensed her father's needs and understood the arrangement. Which didn't mean that things didn't happen. They did. But not *it*. In this at least the measure served its purpose.

The girl never wondered about her mother. She dawdled or sat in a daze when not occupied with a fixed task. She did what had to be done and didn't think about her situation. Maybe *position* is a better word. She accepted her position in the way that she learned and repeated the preparation of meals and other basic jobs from a village woman. Her father had crashed in from time to time on the two as the woman recited her explanations. His daughter being allowed near any other person worried him. It robbed him of that strong YOU he usually flung around the house. *"Are ye right,"* he was forced to shout, waving his arms. There was no such thing as ordinary talking in the house, ever. The girl felt her own words pull back into the quiet inside her head, where a milky calm lapped in the cup of her skull.

When the girl began to menstruate, her father got angry and frightened. He made signs to her from a distance to stay away. He wouldn't even allow her inside the yard. He had the dogs on his side, vicious unreliable mountain dogs that were famous for *turning* and *worrying* and that line of thing. The woman was sent for again. She showed the girl how to make rag pads and where to bury them when they were soiled. Her father was never to see the blood, she was told.

Fogerty was the man's name. The girl had no name, or maybe something very short. She was known as *Fogerty's young one*. Fogerty was an important man in the area. He owned an amount of land and ran the men on it. They also stank of shit. He was locally hated. Hate is a form of appreciation.

The occupation of the Island Republic following the alliance didn't change local life much. The new authorities didn't need to replace rural heads. They preferred to turn them. Fogerty had plenty of time for the leather-coated strangers who talked to him in bad careful sentences. Good straight men. Crucify the troublemakers. In return for their help he offered them his daughter.

His daughter stood along with him at the crucifixions. The troublemakers were bound to T-shaped frames with spirals of barbed wire. The villagers stood close around. Fogerty saw them turn now and again to stare at his daughter, the men's eyes narrowing, and he hated her for the attention she got. After the erection of the crosses he went to speak to the major.

There is now a scene in the main street of the village. The authorities have declared a celebration, with free food and drink. The villagers are worried, but greedy in these hard times. Hunks of dark bread are mounded in large wicker baskets. Three officers stand with a dark brew slopping from their polystyrene beakers. Obviously they don't drink it. They're just *putting in an appearance.* As they talk their eyes turn to greet Fogerty. He offers them his daughter. She's a weight on him. He has no hopes for her. They'll be able to *make something out of her.* Despite their leather coats, the officers aren't sophisticated men. They size her up and decide immediately that she's too young and indistinct to be of interest. They might plaster her with lipstick, and powder her, or dress her in red and black. But she would fall away too easily from behind all this, a small sagging non-person.

The major, a man with a face like a washed-out rag, turns to Fogerty to give his decision. The major prides himself on being a good judge of character. This, as always, means practically that when dealing with people he makes quick and unchangable decisions which protect him from anything unclear. Vagueness would threaten his authority and manhood, which are, as it is, in bad shape. If he turned down the farmer's offer — obviously a form of primitive treaty between the local strongman and the authorities — he could risk giving offence. He says they will take her in tow. She stares at them out of her glue-coloured face. They put her in a cell in the barracks and seem to forget about her.

Days later the youngest of the three officers visits the girl in her quarters. He finds her filthy, well-fed, and quiet. He orders her to be washed and deloused. An eruption on her cheek is lanced and dressed. She's reclothed in brown fatigues. In the evening he drives the girl to the pierhead where a trawler is waiting. For very little money the trawlermen say they will take her across to the continent, to the Lowlands Republic. The officer doesn't do all of this because he cares about the girl.

She's an irregularity in his barracks. He's taking this opportunity, in any case, to present himself to himself as a bit of a character: original and unpredictable. Cruel but merciful. He has a glass eye and a limp and his breath smells of wet dog. Once across the water the trawlermen can do with her what they like. He's done his bit and she'll just have to take her chances.

The crossing is rough. The girl is kept near the anchor locker. She can look down into a sort of trench and see the dark links of chain coiled there. When the boat is hit by a squall she hears the chain unsettle. There's a stink of fishwater and machine oil, and from the start she's sick. She vomits for two days into a blue plastic bucket. Then she keeps down some tea and bread. The men don't much like having her on the boat. Unlike the officers, they find her exciting, although this doesn't mean that they're sophisticated. They just think they maybe could lie on top of her and she would disappear under them. She's locked away so as to avoid rivalry between the crew. The man who brings her the food can't help himself, though. It's nothing too bad. What her father, or some of the men used to go in for. With the hand, he says. *The,* not *your.* It smells afterwards from the bucket.

At daybreak on the fourth day they tie up in the shelter of a stone jetty that juts straight out from a line of strand. Beyond the strip of shingle lies an empty plain of light brown grass. The sea is squally, slate grey. As the girl jumps ashore her face and hands are cut by the salt-heavy wind. A crowd of locals are waiting on the jetty. They exchange bags and boxes for crates of fish. She feels these people might be dangerous. She's right. The trawler falls away out to sea. She follows the knot of traders to the strand where they show her off. A young boy throws a flat stone in her direction in a half-hearted way. His father pulls him on. The stone slithers over the sand near her, cutting a damp trail. She crouches down and watches them disappear in their trucks. When the motor rumble fades she stands up and walks along the shore on legs that feel light and unreliable after days at sea.

The girl's life has been so miserable and so hopeless that in one way it seems funny. Not for her, of course. But it's hard not to ask *What can they possibly do to her next?* The fact is that what happens to her next isn't bad, compared to everything up to now, even if it doesn't make everybody happy.

She stands at the edge of a saltmarsh in the evening. The sky glows purple and brown. Blocky trucks hurtle past, leaving her shuddering and breathless. The stubble of the marshgrass is black against the silver of water and the grey of mud. The road is wide and raised up over the surrounding flats. There is a sort of walkway, a footpath, on the hard shoulder. When night falls she sees long shadows swaying towards her. As they come near she realizes they are women, thinner and taller than any human beings she's ever seen. Their faces are dead still and small blue flames lick from open mouths marked out by thick paint. They walk in a haze of raw alcohol. They puff on black cigarettes, exhale, and a tongue of light shows. Although the girl doesn't know this, they are *frows,* huge women who sell their bodies to truckers. They're terminally addicted to the only available forms of alcohol and will drink cleaning fluids and industrial spirits. They walk the highways of the North, in the Lowlands Republic, clicking their heels along the asphalt that leads to the South, where it's warm.

Next morning a truck stops for her. She sees two figures in the large box of the driver's cabin sheltered from the clear northern light outside. She can't make them out. Teeth smile in the gloom. The face leans over to open the passenger-side door. A brown face, black hair long around the stubbly cheeks. Eyes like tar bubbles on a hot day. Tattoo on a stringy forearm. He signals for her to get in.

They drive south on huge grey stretches of motorway. She finds room between them easily. They don't touch her, and even though she can't understand a word they're saying, there's no feeling of trouble about these people and the air in the cabin is light. They eat small bundles of dried meat and drink clean-tasting water from a plastic drum. The lorry is parked, high up on a rise over a stretch of carefully farmed land cut by giant electric pylons.

They drive into the night and stop in a clump of small pine trees. A warm moist wind carries the sound and smell of the sea to here. The small men climb back like monkeys into a space they use for sleeping. They hand her a blanket and an inflatable cushion. She wakes in the night to hear sounds of wriggling and popping coming from behind her.

The three walk blinking down a gradual slope of white sand. The sun is strong and she feels it hot on her scalp. The men squat down on a smooth sea-log that lies half-buried in the strand. She wanders on picking up a bit of drift-wood with an end like three uneven claws. She scribbles with it in the wet sand, using the points. She doesn't know how to write. She knows the look of it, but it means nothing. She walks out over the empty beach, trailing the stick from one hand and then another, dragging out a broken line behind her. She stops and concentrates. She makes a big E and a stroke that might be the beginning of another letter.

After a while the men stand up and drop fuming butts at their feet. They look around for the girl, but she's disappeared. They trot over the strand with worried faces, squinting into the distance at rocks and dots that refuse to become her.

Aidan Hynes

The Journey Back

Since she'd emigrated to New York Claire Hendron hadn't socialised much. It wasn't that she was an unsociable animal, but that she distanced herself from the cliques and Irish pubs that inundated her area in Queens. She disliked what she regarded as the exaggerated sense of oneness among the expatriates; what she percieved to be an aberration of the reality... cursory unions tempered with sentimentality.

She and Enda lived in Woodside, sometimes referred to as little Ireland, or Ireland in exile. She didn't see much of Ireland about it. She saw restaurants that offered Irish breakfast and shops that maintained a shelf or two for Irish products. She saw happy, sad, serious and drunk faces, black and white... the faces of the world. But Ireland in exile was not Ireland. Little Ireland shared the streets with little Korea, little China, little Columbia, little Paraguay, and yet she saw little of the melting pot as she'd imagined and hoped for; ethnic groups were as isolated and defined as the borders and oceans that separated their countries of origin. For a time New York had been a variant, a place where she and Enda could leave behind their distinct and insular histories, family prejudices and the confinement that comes with homogeneity. They needed time, time to allow wounds to heal and work to be forgotten. But time improved nothing.

His friends didn't like her. They found it difficult to understand, much less respect, her. Being courteous but distant, she eluded them. They finally decided she was a snob; a bourgeois, convent-educated, Galway girl who looked down on their Dublin working-class roots.

Two years after the wedding she'd chanced a visit home. Being an illegal resident in New York exposed her to the rigors of immigration officials on her return flight. But it was worth taking the chance. She loved Ireland. Unlike her sister Bridget, she had little appetite for exploration and travel. She found security in a wet evening on Galway's Shop Street, meeting friends and arranging the night. The week she arrived home the Arts Festival was on; the city was alive with theatre, national and international poets, Spanish comedians, children's panto-mime, street regalia, pub music sessions. She forgot America. But the hoped-for re-establishment of relations with her parents, in particular with her father, had not been successful. Despite herself, she needed his respect and understanding more than anything, and though he was tolerant, indeed generous in his welcoming of her, she knew he'd not forgiven.

The day of their wedding father had feigned sickness; a sickness that she'd married a policeman, an ex-policeman, but still a policeman for all that. Father was a veterinarian; a large, rumbustious man who probably had as many enemies as he had friends. He kept an expansive library of history and republican literature. When one entered the house the framed photographs of ten dead hunger strikers imposed in the hallway. He'd had it replace the 1916 Proclamation of the Irish Republic. As a young girl she'd witnessed the police come and take him away. He returned a week later. No one spoke of it in the family. Apart from the many reminders, he kept his politics to himself. That was until her marriage. The squad car still patrolled the area where they lived; occasionally it paused outside their gateway. It was a strange home where two sisters grew up in the precarious existence of never knowing the day they'd visit their father under the supervision of prison guards; a strange house that occasionally entertained strange faces who slept in the back room and were often gone by dawn.

Mother was a dreamer. For years she and father had slept in separate rooms. When rare occasion demanded, they politely spoke to one another, like colleagues might at work. Claire could never relate to her, could never feel at ease with her, unlike Bridget who treated her with something akin to disdain, and ironically gained her mother's respect. Claire feared her, feared her long silences, her coldness and heedlessness; her conceit that the world deserved only her contempt. Mother's family were wealthy. She'd married very young. Her gentleman-husband drank her money and himself into an early grave. Abandoned by her family, she was left destitute. Then father came along and fell in love.

She'd been so distracted by her new patient that she'd forgotten to collect little Julie after work. Doreen, the baby-sister, brought the child home. Enda usually collected the girl but this evening he was playing a football game. It was the final of something, some league... she didn't take an interest in the event. At any rate he'd simply muttered something about it that morning as she was leaving for work.

She liked the matter-of-fact quality the Northern Ireland woman possessed. You could talk with Doreen and trust that what you said wasn't going to get repeated. They drank tea and discussed her new and difficult patient while little Julie ran in and out of the room, her fair hair, the colour of her mother's, tied in a moon-curved pony-tail. When Doreen took her leave Claire read a fairy-tale to the child until she felt her eyes close.

She found her work menial. Twice she'd failed the American nursing examinations which prevented her from working in the hospitals and obtaining a green card. She worked for an agency, taking private cases and getting paid as a nurse's aide. She needed time and commitment for study. She had neither.

The future seemed bleak. She wanted to go home, resettle, now that time had thwarted her initial plans, had levelled rather than cultivated their passion and dreams.

At first he said he'd follow her to the ends of the earth, to hell and back if need be. But in a world of chance and experience she'd come to see such unwavering intensity burn itself out.

Since they'd left Ireland, Enda's contact with his family had been rare. Stubborn and temperamental, he lacked the courage to make amends. One of six children, his mother had been widowed when Enda was eleven years old. A roofer by trade, his father was killed when he fell four storeys on a job. The family lived in a two-bedroomed house off the North Circular Road on Dublin's north side. The children were nourished on a widow's pension, and educated by an older sister, Eileen, a lowly-paid civil servant. Hardly a day passed without the family being reminded by their stoic though able mother that job security was the prelude to a happy life.

Just weeks before the wedding, he and Claire had to make a troubling visit to his home. He was the bearer of sour tidings; he, the proud result of his mother's philosophy on life, the fulfill-ment of his sister's effort, had betrayed the fundamental required for a happy existence.

He'd never felt such outrage as he experienced that evening. Having told them of his dismissal, and being at odds with the heavy silence that followed, he'd gone with a younger brother to the shop to buy cigarettes. Unwittingly he'd left Claire to face a provoked mother and Eileen. They couldn't help themselves, couldn't hold back now that their long held doubts and apprehensions about her had finally been substantiated. They confronted and condemned her and her "terrorist" family for his dismissal from the force. He'd known the truth of it, but at the time a nation's prerequisites of its servants could not displace the ungovernable terrain of passion. They accused her of pressurizing him into marriage. She was a poor choice indeed; with her he'd lost all sense of responsibility. She'd made no reply, persevering in a disbelief at their revealing wrath, yet the more they rebuked and wounded, the more she was tempted to counter-attack, to tell them how she was with child. But with respect to keeping the matter concealed, she held back.

Only for his sake would they be attending the wedding, if a wedding there must be. They wished she'd disappear. She got up and left.

Enda had been suspended from the force after he'd smashed the squad car when giving chase to joyriders. The mockery of it all was that the chief decided he'd been driving recklessly. Later he was asked to leave or face prosecution. Left in little doubt that they wanted to weed out an "unreliable member" with a passion for an I.R.A. man's daughter, he put up no defence and left.

He said he didn't care and perhaps he didn't, then. But with time she'd come to discern his erratic moods and repressed temper, like an itch tormenting him, a festering resentment. She thought at first it might be of Ireland, but later came to consider that she too was involved. She was John Hendron's daughter. As his mother and sister would have it, wasn't she a product of John Hendron's politics and deceptive character?... a progeny of the man who gave a two-fingered salute to the powers he could so wilily outmaneuvre; powers that Enda had proudly defended — powers that outmaneuvred him.

Only once had he stepped inside her home, a couple of days after the unpleasant events in Dublin. Naively she'd hoped it would be reconciliation of sorts, her circumspect attempt to have father appreciate the man his enemies had recently dismissed, a man who said he could care less. While Enda might duly share her frustration and resentment at his family's blunt criticism, his manner was equally as abrupt when it came to the obligatory visit with her father. She was now on her own, striving to please two men, anticipating friction, a second condemnation... even if more subtle, still no less brutal.

She recalled how stonily Enda had sat in that chair facing father; Janus-faced father, a saint could not have been more humble. He'd played the perfect host with his spirited attentions on his soon to be son-in-law. It seemed she needn't have held back the information on her lover all this time. Father was unduly civil, deferential yet noticeably interested in their future plans. Considering over events she wondered at the mind of her father; had he been there and then contemplating the greatest insult she'd ever received?... the incident that finally determined her journey to America.

That same evening mother had hidden in her room. But it was father who mattered. She loved him. For all her later hurt and anger, she loved him that he'd singly tried to raise them. From a young age she fancied he'd not had a wife, and being a romantic she was moved to pity. She wanted to be as good as a wife to him, to replace her mother, to spite her. It was her defence against the fear she had of her and therefore the need to have his attentions.

At any rate, that he'd kept family and politics independent from each other all those years, was it not reasonable to think he'd continue to do so?

Things changed after the trip home. Life took on a new meaning, or the meaninglessness of their lives together suddenly struck her. And when it did, she came to realize her vulnerability, her ineffectiveness at what confronted her. Somewhere they'd lost one another. She didn't know him, and to her surprise there were times when she wished she never had. Both of them had changed because both had different agendas.

Everything had become alien to her... her family, his family, New York; official America described her as an alien; she alienated herself and was in turn alienated by others. She would not participate in her new society; she'd never intended it to be her home.

She treasured the weekly letter from Bridget in Spain. Bridget taught English in Barcelona, wrote and published her poetry, lived bohemian. They were worlds apart. She envied Bridget, as much as she tried to convince herself she didn't. It was her freedom, a freedom she'd worked to maintain, leaving home at the earliest opportunity. Not that Claire minded at first; she continued her illusive role of companion to her father, coming home after her shift at the hospital and cooking his dinner, when even mother invited herself to the occasional meal with them; then after dinner getting ready to meet with her new lover, the young policeman recently stationed in the city. They met at a friend's housewarming.They'd been going out for a year before she'd told father. It was the first time she'd kept a secret of her boyfriends from him. He was always amused to hear about them, and enjoyed meeting with them. But he was frazzled about her sudden lack of communication. He'd often ask if she'd given up on the gender. And when she'd say no, there would be tension between them. She'd come to feel a certain reserve, even intimidation, now that her father's politics had come to affect her adult life. She felt defeat that she could not talk to him, to feel as free as hitherto; to tell him how happy she felt, how decent and sincere Enda was.

With Bridget it was different. But then Bridget was different. Nobody would dare interfere with her sovereignty. And she had such an easy standing at home; an almost pusillanimous respect was afforded her by both mother and father. She demanded it; her art allowed for it. For all her iconoclastic ways, she was admired as the wayward star.

Again she envied that her father simply muted when Bridget espoused the benefits of pacifism. But then Bridget's pacifism did not mean she was politically passive, and she and father could readily identify on issues of justice and ambiguity in current political affairs. Claire was apolitical; she didn't want to, nor did she pretend to, understand the world she was brought up in. But it mystified her that the same world was now condemning her earlier apathy, or better, innocence; torn between the expectations and ideology of the two men whom she simply wanted to love.

Bridget travelled much. Last year she'd been to New York. She'd stayed with a friend in Manhattan. Claire understood. Bridget felt uncomfortable with Enda. They'd never hit it off. Their first encounter was a mutual understanding of opposites: personality, politics, feminism, objectives.

One night she and Claire got drunk in Manhattan. They laughed and chatted as never before. They'd become inseparable, Claire, at twenty-eight, the prettier and younger by two years, recognised reciprocal needs; the need to be loyal and frank, to be protective of one another as they'd both shared an erratic and precarious upbringing. It was during that visit she retrieved some of her former spontaneity, the whimsies that love had ironically suppressed and exile suspended. She could joke on the bizarre relationship of her parents, and as much as she tried to understand and respect his family's wounded pride, she derided their attempt at moral superiority... anyone's attempt at moral superiority, her father's, her mother's... realizing how needlessly she'd travelled 3,000 miles to escape from that.

Sometimes after they'd make love he'd cry as he sank on her. She 'd comb his light brown hair with her fingers and kiss his eyes. He was her little boy, her sensitive, passive little boy. So he'd been since their first time in bed; she was his first experience. His shy and open nature conquered her as much as she was surprised that at twenty-four he'd been pure boy; the boy who at first had made all the solicitations for dates. There were endless nights when he cried and she kissed his eyes; she'd metamorphosised the dispassionate policeman by day into her febrile lover by night. Initially he was sensitive to caution, keen to humour her whims and desires. He was the student; but when the student became a partner, he threw caution to the wind, and with passion refused to withdraw, refused to use condoms and she refused to use the pill.

In the relative few years they'd been together, that was all in the past.

Occasionally a brooding man came home. He'd don the cloak of silence, and if she tried to talk with him, he angered swiftly.

Sometimes he drank too much and he'd sit up until late listening to traditional music and ballads. He'd creep into bed, his back to her. She knew he cried then too, but the tears were too bitter for resolution, and she left him alone.

Following the initial furore over his dismissal from the force he'd never spoken of it since. She wished he would. She imagined there to be a voice goading him, eating into a harassed conscience, and she feared it; she feared its motivation, the possible excuses set forth that "she" was the prime cause of his pariah status with family and country. She knew how much he'd loved that job. When dating he'd often said how fulfilled he felt. Power? she once asked him. Of course not, he'd rejoined. He was doing something worthy.

She recognized the loss of dignity, of power too. In New York he'd managed to join the carpenter's union. Now he was a carpenter, the captain of a football team, an exile among exiles on the sidewalks and bars in Queens.

She began to feel intimidated. He'd become more demanding with her... perturbing, crude in a way. At times he made her feel almost prudish, drove her to exasperation and anger. She longed for the boy, the sensitive soul of the discriminating lover. The boy grown man, like some crass stranger, unnerved her. He wanted experimentation with their sex. Allow him to tie her up, initiate foreplay, master sexual inhibition. She said she'd not known she had any. He said they should swap partners, place advertisements in the appropriate magazines, *ménage á trois*. She demanded he stop, and reminded him how little he'd thought of her inhibitions when they first met. His face darkened and he walked away. Then she wanted to apologise. But she couldn't, she felt neither prudish nor inhibited. She felt normal, maybe. It confused her.

In the evening silences, the now dry and spurious sex, she felt wooden, a burden to the boy grown man, desensitized man, and what was left of their relationship lacked even the accommodation of her own parents.

He'd always respected her privacy; her inheritance he'd say sarcastically. He'd never bring friends back to the apartment after drinking. But with others he'd become more friendly; with her, more defiant. Like last week when he'd brought some friends from the football team home. It was one o'clock in the morning. She'd been sleeping. At first she heard the voices, soft and respectful as they settled themselves into the front room. Then a wave of alcohol hit her when he came into the bedroom. Her immediate reaction was one of anger. Hadn't they all work to go to in the morning? she'd wanted to know. He sat on the bed. She scolded more and he stiffened. He wanted sandwiches. Incredulous, she refused. His eyes narrowed, deep lines sweeping across his forehead. He demanded. She relented, resigned to the alternative of a nasty argument, and hated her weakness of spirit, the humiliation of it all... cook and aide by day, cook and hostess by night to his friends. She hated them, and he'd become one of them. And then that sickening volte-face, his fazed perception of who and what she was, and who and what she'd become for him, he kissed her, and kissed her breasts as she got out of bed, telling her she was a dream.

Having made the sandwiches, she'd been drinking a glass of milk when Tom Brennan strutted into the kitchen. A work colleague of Enda's, he was a wiry, sickly looking individual. Someone had begun to sing, poorly; cans of beer popped. She thought to go into them, to demand they leave, but she dared not; she dared not do battle with what she imagined would be a volley of scathing, leering eyes assaulting and rebutting her, her husband's among them.

"You're not joining us?" Tom Brennan said ironically. He grinned while his drunken eyes swam over her. "No, I've work to go to in the morning," she'd replied snappily. He circled the table in the middle of the kitchen and took a sandwich.

"Maybe we're not good enough for you," he said and came up to her. She was determined to remain cool.

"Is that what you think?"she answered. "Perhaps you're right." He continued to grin, taking on a monkeyish posture. She asked him to take the sandwiches into the other room, adding her appreciation if he'd encourage the chanters to keep their voices down. There was a child sleeping. Suddenly he gripped her by the arm and brought his ashen lips to her ears. "I'll take you into another room if you like," he gurgled. She pushed him away. "Pig!" she spat out. He laughed as she rushed from the kitchen just when little Julie was calling her name.

That night she'd slept with the frightened child; frightened from the noise and the dark. She'd wrapped the child in her arms and gently rocked her to sleep, and continued to rock herself into a seething anger. Then she heard him sing. He was singing "Carrickfergus". She stopped swaying and listened attentively. He'd always a temperate voice, sweet in timbre, steady as a drum beat. His singing hushed any audience. It struck her for the first time, the lyrics, the intense feeling and respect he could have with that song. That great desire to be with a loved one, to be across the ocean to woman and country, to love and die, to readily admit defeat in exile, and she wondered why... why so far away before love could ignite such emotion, such beauty. Was it an apology for betrayal on one's own doorstep? And was the room suddenly filled with some celestial light of truth that drunken men were muted by the moment in a song? This beauty corrupted, provoked but a moment's awakening in the dead. And she pondered this and more another hour and two while the singers left one by one until she fell into a troubled sleep.

The following morning they'd had their worst argument, accusing each other in turn of disrespect, dismissing one another as spoilers and liars. He'd said how there had been little noise, and that Tom Breenan was only fooling about while she was being a bitch. He was being a bastard. She told him she'd leave him, she was going home and he'd better make up his mind about that. He said she was crazy, and with derision asked what home she had to go to. They'd hardly spoken since. Day after day a growing disquiet, his obstinacy on the one hand, her resolution one minute to do what she'd threatened, then fear the next minute at the consequences. A week when she'd taken to sleeping with little Julie, explaining to the inquisitive child how there was a deep hole on her side of the bed. "And can't Daddy fix it?" the child wanted to know. "When he's ready," she answered.

She'd called the nursing agency about her patient. She wanted to be taken off the case. But the agent said how lucky she was to have a case, work was scarce and the woman hung up.

Mrs Getshin lived on Manhattan's upper east side. She'd been a widow since Wall Street's Black Monday. Having lost half an empire, her husband had readily collapsed and taken his leave of the world. A large portrait of him hung in the dining-room, the artist depicting a man at ease with his environment; ruddy cheeked, mustachioed and balding; his short frame in a white suit leaning on a black cane, an idyllic landscape to his rear. The benign smile would have the viewer understand that the dominions of Wall Street and real estate had little effect in the life of this rococo portrait. The apartment was old, rich in artifacts, lush green and pink carpets, spacious rooms with quaint furnishings.

Claire's day rarely varied. Help Mrs Getshin out of bed, wash her down, cook her breakfast, launder her clothes. Mrs Getshin, an astute and calculating woman, was in her seventies. She said she preferred the European nurses... more professional. For Claire the truth of this apparent prejudice was that Mrs Getshin was not unaware that she was getting the qualified nurse who worked in the country illegally. Mre Getshin got double her money's value; the nurse as aide and cook... the nurse more attentive to the whims of her patient who had the wherewithal to call the immigration authorities at will.

Porridge too hot, too cold, too thick, too thin. Toast overdone, underdone, moist, hard. Put Mrs Getshin back to bed. Sit next to her while she sleeps. Give her the dozen assortment of pills. Take her out of bed, wash her down again, dress her up, put her into the wheelchair, a walk to Central Park... wheelchair pushed roughly, too fast, too slow, heedless, nay deliberately pushing Mrs Getshin to a hasty grave. Bring her home at once!

Perhaps Mrs Getshin had cause to complain on this particular day as her nurse was rather listless and inattentive. They'd returned from the daily excursion to Central Park and Claire had settled her into bed. When Mrs Getshin snored Claire got her reprieve, time for a coffee and cigarette, a half hour to herself in the redundant maid's room.

She'd reached the nadir of her frustration. It seemed nothing could get settled; no hope of reconciliation, yet oddly she willed the cold war between Enda and herself to continue. In a curious way it brought her peace; being left alone was freedom in itself. Still it had to end; it was a freedom compounded with tensions.

She wanted to cry but stopped herself, or was stopped by something... perhaps anxiety, and yet she felt a strength, a power, a feeling that she could rise above the conundrum of internal confusion; she could strike out. It was all a matter of how.

Mrs Getshin's phlegmatic voice was shouting her name. Oh if only she could scream! She jumped up and hurried to the room.

"Didn't you hear me calling you? Sleeping were you? I don't employ you to sleep I'll have you know. My leg is sore. Put a compress on it... boil the water." She did as she heard;

automation, kitchen, water, boil, cloth, basin, him, them, song, pain, movement...

"It's not hot enough," Mrs Getshin shouted when Claire fixed the compress to the leg.

"I boiled the water."

"Well boil it more if you did... boil it more I tell you!"

She did as she heard and boiled the boiled water... careful, she told herself, dealing with boiled water, calm, movement, pain, humiliation, them, women, derision. She placed the steaming cloth against the tender area, determined to erase that vein, that pain, that mark from her life. She dipped and rinsed, her hands scalded the more she pressed and raged at vein and pain, in silence and misery until the blood stirred in her cheeks. Mrs Getshin lay on her back, half clad, half dead, holding up with all her wrath a thin, varicose leg. She too reddened with vein and pain, and with the circumstances that brought these two women together, whose increasing hate, helplessness, and frustration with a twilight world necessarily bound them together.

"It's not hot enough! It's not boiled!" Mrs Getshin shouted. Tears came to both women. "I cannot make it any hotter," Claire cried.

"Don't you know how to make a compress? Don't you know how to boil water? What are these agencies sending to me? A simple compress, a very simple compress. Boil the water!"

"I did."

"Boil it! Boil it! Boil it! Damn you!"

"And damn you."

"What?" There was a moment's silence."You dare speak to me like that? You' re fired."

"Fine," Claire answered simply.

"Put me into my chair."

Mrs Getshin wheeled herself to a desk at the other end of the bedroom. She withdrew a cash box from a drawer, counted some bills and pushed them into Claire's hand. To her great indignation Claire stood next to her, counting the money before departing.

"Your agency will hear of this," Mrs Getshin said as Claire was leaving the room. "I'll see that you don't work in this field again young lady. Mark my words on it. I'll be making my calls." Claire presumed the old woman to mean the immigration authorities. So be it she thought, and in slamming Mrs Getshin's front door she felt an inrush of power and a renewed pride.

It was just after midday as she made her way to the 59st subway station. On Lexington Avenue she diverted into a coffee shop. Sitting, stirring her coffee, she breathed a tremendous sigh of relief. Why relief? Surely she had more trouble now than she'd ever bargained for. She'd have to get hold of Enda and tell him, even if she was exaggerating Mrs Getshin's potential to inform immigration. Then the thought struck. It was a moment like one experiences in finding the final clue to a difficult treasure hunt; she grabbed at it. To connive with him would be to lose it, ruin it, spoil it. With his lack of imagination he'd drive them further apart. He'd simply change address. They'd have to move in with friends, his friends, while they acquired another apartment, hiding from official America in order to hide themselves from the reality of their future. She would find it intolerable and ultimately she would have to break with him. He'd said America was his home. There was no going back for him. But there was no going back for her now... no more alien status, no more Mrs Getshins, no more Tom Brennans, no more sentiment and disappointment, not another day with another assault on her freedom.

The waiter refilled her cup. She was going to be brave, to strike out; she'd repair their relationship or abandon it. She saw it unravel before her. She would make the first move, for the three of them.

She'd go to Doreen's and collect little Julie. She'd tell Doreen the truth... as much of it as she need tell her. From their conversation the previous evening, losing the case wouldn't surprise her anyway. Later Enda would arrive only to hear Doreen tell of Mrs Getshin's potential threat.

Two days ago Bridget's letter had arrived. Come over, she'd insisted... you need a break. You and I need to get drunk again... we're too far away, too alone, too caught up with the world.

A stiff brandy... later. Time to think, no. She was finished with time. Another cigarette... go now for God's sake. Little Julie would never understand. Every child needs a holiday, and a mother. And him? His move. You're a coward. His move. There's much to do. One-way tickets. To the travel agents. He knows how to be careful.

That evening at J.F.K. she had that brandy. She and an excited little Julie were about to board a flight for Spain. Daddy would follow, she'd told the child. And if he did she'd welcome him. He'd made his move. She'd called Bridget earlier. She was on her way, details later.

As the plane took off from the runway she recalled the hurried letter she'd sealed in an envelope and left on the kitchen table for him. She wasn't proud of it, the haste and scrawled details, the request he follow, the confusion, the consequences of her taking the child. She was not proud that she couldn't face him. She tried to console herself that it was for them both, the hackneyed adage, cruelty in kindness. No, she wasn't proud of anything just then, but she very much looked forward to seeing her sister.

Eamonn Wall

Four paintings by Danny Maloney

The four paintings hanging on the walls in the Goldstein Gallery made no sense to me on opening night, but neither did any of the others by the rest of the artists who were part of the show. I looked at Danny Maloney's and nodded my head at what caught my eye, or at something I recognized — like the odd lavender curtains and sheets in a hotel room, at the East River and the Brooklyn Bridge. When I noticed his ring in the corner of one painting, I looked closer and found the shape of his hand buried under the newspaper. A hole had been slit in the newspaper, big enough for me to see the ring on the little finger of his left hand: his drinking hand. The Downtown crowd distracted me: shrieking, hugging, calling, waving, and talking loudly about each other's doings and what they would do afterwards. "Are you going on to the opening down the street?" a women asked me. They fascinated me: I wandered about eavesdropping on their small talk and studying their clothes — bought at Bergdorf's, estate sales, at Goodwill. Scarves are in and black cowboy boots.

I was also thinking of my husband at home, way uptown in the Inwood Section, putting the children to bed, laughing to myself: what a lark he'd have looking at this crowd. It didn't faze me that I knew no one. Of course, seeing *his* paintings connected me to the opening, gave me a reason to be here. And Danny Maloney wasn't present; there was no set of blue eyes telling me I had to say something smart. I don't need to do that anymore. I talk to my family now, and to my First Grade class in the school on Vermileya Avenue — the school with the bars on the windows, chains on the doors, and a security man in a chair at the door who directs all visitors to the office. My life in my home neighbourhood. New York City.

Grace Maloney told me about the exhibition, that she'd gotten a letter and a catalogue from the Gallery. She wrote and said she'd asked the gallery to invite me to the opening since I was the only person she knew in New York except for her cousins on Seaman Avenue and they wouldn't be interested in going anyway. I was still angry with her for not telling me about what had happened to Danny, for not even telling me he was sick so I could have visited him. She said no one knew till he was dead. I never believed her: Grace always knows. She spent her life tracking his every move. Her brother! A year later, one Saturday morning in the playground in Inwood while the children were digging in the sandbox, she told me the story. She said that when he died she and her parents had come to New York and spent a weekend in an apartment down the street from me. She hadn't called. The Irish family: it draws you in, then it shuts you out. Standing together against the world.

I set aside another day to see the paintings. One Saturday, my husband came downtown with me on the train. I left him at the Canal St. Station with the boys and gave him the following instructions: to walk around Chinatown showing them the produce stands, the fish, and the live crabs in the white buckets. When they got hungry, there was a MacDonald's on Canal. Buy each of them a toy from the street vendors. He said he'd also bring them to Canal Jeans on Broadway to look for T-Shirts. I told him I'd be at 580 Broadway, that I'd meet him at the coffee shop on the corner in three hours.

Grace on the park bench, drinking soda that day had said: "We took a taxi in from the airport to the hospital and went upstairs and sat in a room and a black women asked us if we wanted coffee, where we were after coming from, were we tired. The folks said nothing. Daddy hadn't said a word since we'd got the news, and Mammy only spoke to me when Daddy was gone. I was thinking to myself how weird it was — to be in New York in a hospital called St. Vincent's, just like at home, and with the holy pictures on the walls, the crucifixes, and the pictures of John Paul II everywhere."

"In the village," I told her.

"With the bags piled in the corner, not being able to smoke. And it was so quiet. You couldn't hear the traffic on the street. The freezing air flowing through the room, even though it was scorching outside."

"It's a famous hospital," I said, "where Dylan Thomas died. That's where the boys were born."

The first painting I looked at is called "Stones". In the centre of the canvas stand a bunch of grey boulders. Above them the sky is mostly grey too, though a lighter grey than the stones, and with patches of fluffy white here and there. In circles around the stones are rows of pebbles, then tufts of grass, then deep green grass. No figures. An Irish landscape? What does it mean? Of course, when I looked back on it I guessed that this first painting was an Irish scene to tell people that Danny Maloney was Irish. The painting was as cold as Danny was when he talked about Ireland, or "home," as he spitefully called it. When you think of Ireland, you are supposed to think of the green fields. But you could just as easily think of the stones and the rocks you see everywhere. Stones that are the colour of the weather, representing Irish silences: the man from Carlow I fell in love with who couldn't hold me when I felt weak, who could never say the words I needed to hear. One year was enough there. I'm glad I didn't stay. The grass at the edges of this painting is a drug. It's like heroin — calming, deflective, warming the stones. But the cold grey stone — cold and strong — is Ireland. Is the man standing at his front door, smoking his pipe, smiling at you? His shiny clothes. His nodding wife making cups of tea.

"It's time for the *News* Charlie," I hear her call.

"After an age," Grace said, "the door opened and two men came in. My father looked at the floor. I stood up. One man said he was sorry for our grief or something odd like that and then said, 'Here's the death certificate. Mr. O'Brien will help with the other details,' and he walked out. I looked at Mr O'Brien. A man in his forties wearing a sports coat and a pair of grey trousers, like anyone you'd meet at home. He looked at us all. I smiled. Mammy nodded. Daddy said nothing; he just dug his hands into the arms of the chair the same way he'd dug them into the side of the seat on the plane. Daddy who'd always wanted to come to America. Mr O'Brien sat down and took a folder from his case. He said: 'Danny Maloney was a good friend of mine. A good friend of many in our community in New York. When people got sick, he visited them. That was his way of helping. When he got sick, we took care of him. Friends brought him his meals, bathed him, changed his sheets, helped him with his bills. In the hospital, one of us was always there to hold his hand. Up to the end. We wanted him to get in touch with you, but he said we shouldn't — he was worried about what you'd say if you saw him.' He sighed and looked at me. 'I have his will,' he said. 'He asked me to sell his possessions and donate the money to an organization here in the city which helps people who get sick. Some of his paintings will be exhibited next year and the proceeds...' He stopped".

The second painting was the largest on display. "Immigrants" is its title, and it is divided into distinct panels. You follow it from left to right. In the first panel, a mass of people is seen walking on the Brooklyn Bridge in the direction of Manhattan. They are holding banners and placards. You cannot see a face or make out what's written. You see blurs and lines. But the grey sky and water are clearly visible. The second focuses on the deep black faces of the marchers. They are Haitians. In the third panel are some cops standing on the sidewalk, watching the marchers. They have that bored look on their faces of all the officers of the NYPD. In the final panel, a man is on the platform speaking into a microphone outside Federal Plaza. I remember this march: when thousands of Haitians walked from Brooklyn to the offices of the INS calling for an end to discrimination against them. They did not deserve to be punished for the presence of AIDS in this country. The marchers are bright, colourful, and noble in the painting: the rest of the world is drab. Politics! Something Danny Maloney never cared about. Or maybe just Irish Politics. But when you're gay in America today, and an immigrant, you're involved in politics whether you like it or not. This is a more hopeful painting than "Stones". Danny looks at the Caribbean people and loves them in a way he can't love the Irish, his own people. They're exotic. I remember seeing a video on MTV of U2. They were singing with a black choir in Harlem. Can't remember the song. Maybe it was "I Still Haven't Found What I'm Looking For". They come to America, embrace the downtrodden, and leave. It does Bono's ego some good, but that's about it. I teach the children of men and women who have died of AIDS: shooting up, fucking, dying. Each day. But I'm happy with Danny Maloney when I think of him bringing food to a sick man's house, holding the hand of a dying friend in St. Vincent's, the Poor Clare's, or at St. Luke's. Sickness and loneliness changed his life. Bono goes home first class; Danny travels in the cargo hold.

Danny Maloney. One night when I was a student in Dublin Grace brought you along to Mulligan's. You told me all about the New York I cared little about — the museums, the galleries, life in the village. You knew them better than I who had seen them without ever caring for them. My world: Inwood, Good Shepherd Church and School, Bronx science, Fordham University. Going downtown to eat, shop, and see the movies, entering enemy territory. I spent a year in Ireland because I won a scholarship my father insisted I apply for: he thought it would be good for me to "experience" his homeland. I prefer the Bronx Irish to the New Ross Irish. Danny Maloney told me he wanted to live in New York.

"Daddy looked up. 'What are ye saying this for,' his voice hoarse and breaking. 'He's dead,' We don't know you,' Who sent you to talk to us?' 'Danny, Mr Maloney ...' 'Maybe you didn't hear me. We don't want you here. Isn't that right, Joan?' My mother said, 'It would be better if you left us alone.' I told him I'd talk with him. We went to another room, but I didn't know what to say. I was thinking of the cheek of that fella coming to the hospital and confronting us like that. It was only making things worse for us all. Like it was a conspiracy. He asked me if I wanted any of Danny's personal effects. I said I didn't. Did we want to see the body. I went and asked Daddy. He said: 'All the arrangements are taken care of. We are taking the body home on Sunday. Now tell that man to get out of our sight'. That was it then: we had until tomorrow to wait to get the plane home."

She didn't want any of her brother's personal effects! Imagine that! Why? Whenever he was home Danny and his father went fishing together. They came home happy, smelling of beer. I remember the two of them laughing together in the yard as they cleaned out the fish. The family that adopted me in Ireland, that invited me down the country.

The third painting is called "Home". A young man is caught in the act of taking off his T-shirt. His head is covered by it, his back is deeply tanned. The bed sheets and curtains are lavender. Outside under a grey sky you can see the Empire State Building. Danny Maloney is sitting on a chair watching. You can't see him in the painting, but you can see his ring through a slit in *The New Ross Standard,* which is open on the table in front of him. To live as he wanted to is why he came to America, to my back door. One night in his parents' house he came to my room and we made love. What, I wonder, would the Maloney's have thought, if Mr O Brien had not come to see them in the hospital? Danny Maloney's funeral? "Sad, but beautiful," his sister told me. A sunny August morning in New Ross. Heartbreaking when the young are taken away, I imagine the priest saying. The truth is lost.

"That night we had the relative's apartment to ourselves: they were called away suddenly. We ate our dinner and watched television till it was time to go to bed. The next morning we went on the subway to St. Patrick's Cathedral to Mass. We saw the spires when we got out of the station, but when we got up close to it there were police barricades everywhere and a huge crowd roaring and shouting and cursing."

"An ACT UP and QUEER NATION demonstration," I said.

"The police cleared a way through the crowd for the people going to Mass. But the crowd was shouting at us. Daddy was jostled, and white in the face. Can you imagine it, after all he'd been through? When the cardinal was giving his sermon, they started shouting at him. The police came and took them away. Then, during the communion, they got the hosts and spat them out on the altar."

She went on like this. I continued to look across the playground to the sandbox, then to the slides when the boys moved over there to play. This is my park, I was thinking to myself, close to the two rivers, the boathouse, and oak trees.

"After the Mass, we collected our bags from the apartment and took a taxi to the airport. I remember it was 3.00pm when we got there, hours before the plane was due to leave. And it was there that Daddy took to crying."

"It was too late," I said.

She looked at me.

"And what about yourself?" I asked.

"I think of him."

The last painting is entitled "Why I like the Prairie." Under an enormous sky is a cornfield: one which has already been harvested. The stalks stick up at odd angles from the earth: they are turning brown. The earth is black. There are no figures: no people, no cars. Whenever I am reminded of desolation, of being heartbroken and lonely, I hear Randy Travis' voice, in which all of our griefs are harboured. I have this vision of him in my soul on a vast concert tour filling football stadiums with all of my brothers and sisters. After the concert concludes, they drive off into the darkness, tears drying on their faces, but possessed of the powers of description. There is nothing on the prairie; that's why it frightens me. But my husband likes it for just that reason; there you can get away from it all. For Danny Maloney, I guess, the attraction was the same. There was always too much of everything in Ireland (friends, family, history) and in New York (love, death, and people). Here, there is nothing. I know you liked to withdraw. There's nothing on the prairie except yourself. And it is your prairie.

The boys were drinking soda in the café when I met them there. They shouted at me as I walked towards them and showed me their new *Ninja Turtles*. "Hey dudes and dudettes," they sang. My husband was drinking coffee. He smiled at me. In a way, I was glad I'd made this second trip downtown to see these paintings. I looked at my husband, "Hold me close tonight. Whisper over and over — I love you, I love you," I said with my eyes. He knew. As I drank my coffee parts of a song came to me and I chanted them like a prayer:

"Well I lost my heart on the day we met
But I gained a lot that I don't regret
Then I hung around till you said I do
I knew I wouldn't have nothin'
If I didn't have you."

Helena Mulkerns

The Suitcase

Joaquin kicked the air conditioning once more as he passed the window, finally deciding it wasn't worth trying to fix again. Screaming rose through it from the street; the kids from the basement apartment were back from school. How could they rush around like that in this bloody furnace?

He started at his tepid beer, flattening in the heat. He was too lethargic to shift himself to the icebox for another. He listened to the couple next door fighting again. "*¿Cállate, coño, imbécil de mierda!*" "*Y tu madre, pendejo!*" The crashing and shouting had been going on all afternoon. People were animals. Another thud came through the wall followed by a whimper and a door slam. He turned on the radio. A talk show; gimme a break.

"Yes people, it's a hot, hot afternoon all over the Tri-state area, and just a cool 102 degrees here in Midtown. You're listening to "Strictly Personal" with Craig Overcash on your favourite radio station. And before we cut for a little break we have Mrs Marjorie Wilson on the line right now, who wants to tell us about her husband's embarrassing habit..."

He picked up the paper, now several days old. More scandal. "Gays in Panic"— "AIDS corpses disposed of by Army". It was mass hysteria. At this stage, funeral parlours wouldn't take in the stiffs. The mariconcitos were losing jobs — even having problems getting their clothes pressed. It was the only topic everywhere you went, for God's sake, Joaquin was just about sick of it. Why didn't they just get out of everybody's faces and go off to some desert island, or something.

"Okay, Majorie, so this is difficult to relate to, but didn't you realise your husband had this problem before your marriage?"

"Well, Craig, you know..."

"Well, you know, Majorie, fuck that," snapped Joaquin, switching it off. But that didn't do much good since that madwoman Señora Carmen downstairs was listening to the Puerto Rican station. It was pretty fuckan disgusting, this place. Junkies and blacks and weirdos, he was sorry he ever answered the ad for the sublet in the first place. But it was cheap. He'd just better get some work soon, he thought, turning his radio dial viciously. At last, he found Aerosmith on some other station and turned it up full blast to drown out the blaring bugles and advertisements in bad Spanish. He walked over to the icebox, confronted along the way by the flies dining on leftover pizza lunch.

Abruptly, he jerked back and turned off the music as the sound of the phone screeched through the room. The phone. That stupid Mexican woman from the Institute reception last night, maybe.

"Hello? Ah, Señora. Yes, how are you. Yes, of course I remember. Oh sure. Sounds fantastic, I'd love to talk about it. I did that kind of stuff when I worked in Milano — high quality pannelling, finishing — that kind of thing. I even have some pictures of what I've done, I'll bring my *port-a-folio*. Yes, I can make that, okay — see you then..."

He rushed to the clothes line, tied from one window to the door of the bathroom, and cursed as he felt his favourite shirt. Still wet, shit. Never mind. The grey silk one was clean and the black pants. He showered, shaved and fixed the hair carefully. This old sarcófago had to be impressed. He let the machine play for the next call and Marina's gushy Brazilian voice flooded the room. Shit. If she thought he was going off to Eurotrash-ville again tonight she had another thing coming. Things were just about to take off for him now, and she was beginning to be a pain in the ass. Of course, she'd helped him a lot, yeah. Introductions were important. But still.

He brushed the ashes off his portfolio and fished his carefully forged Greencard out of the back of a drawer. Social Security card, Driver's Licence. Joaquin prided himself on being a man that never did things by halves. He got a certain satisfaction out of knowing he was away on a hack — he'd go home at Christmas and find the same vagos on the same stools in the same bars as the night he'd left. Meantime he was wearing the silk shirts. This job looked like a particularly good bet, once he got around this woman. And Joaquin knew he could be more charming than most in 102 degrees. Especially to rich Mexican widows, he told himself.

His neighbour, of all people, was emerging from the elevator as he closed his door. Shooting daggers as he pushed past, he clutched a small bunch of withering flowers. God, just the job for her black eye. The smells turned his stomach as floor after filthy floor passed his eye level through the grid. Obscene graffiti covered the walls and it looked like a dog had puked in one corner.

The stairway which zig-zagged up around the elevator shaft was the darkest place in the building. The only light hitting the walls in the entrance hall slivered through the window above the doorway, which was shut to keep the heat out. On the very top floor the junkies used to come in and shoot up just at the roof exit, so there was sometimes some air if it was left open. But otherwise, without air conditioning, the place just became a dark oven in the pit of the building. It gave Joaquin the creeps. One of these nights...

He slammed the grid shut, and stood a moment in the dimness to light a cigarette. Suddenly, he heard a shuffle on the other side of the hallway. Oh God. He could see nothing. There was a sniff, but still nothing moved. Oh come on, not now, please . . . Reaching out in a panic, he hit the light switch and stepped back quickly, ready to defend himself.

A man was standing a short distance away, supporting himself against the wall. Shoulders slightly hunched, he stared fiercely at Joaquin with, surprisingly, a mixed expression of self-possession and all-consuming terror. Although he was clearly only in his early thirties, he had hair so thin he was almost bald. And the face was ancient — it looked as if it were in an advanced stage of decay. In the garish light of the bulb, it was thrown into dramatic relief — reddened eyes sunken behind protruding cheek-bones with only shadows underneath, emphasizing a horror- movie style emaciation. The skin was a dull grey, broken by large, dark blotches and spots. Joaquin stared at the heavy woollen overcoat; although he held it tightly closed, the man was shivering violently all over. He blinked nervously without moving. His whole aspect evinced a fundamental fact that brought a quick layer of sweat out over Joaquin's newly-showered back.

Joaquin looked away and headed briskly towards the door, in a panic. Fuck. The state of the guy, the state of him.

"Eh — please..."

Heartdive. He hadn't heard; he continued on.

"Eh, please... before you leave..." The man began to speak in excellent, accented Spanish.

He stopped for a moment, not knowing exactly why. It was contagious, you know. But God love the miserable bastard, all the same. Telling himself it was his good deed for the year, he turned around, managing a half smile. This had better be for real. The man hunched forward even more and the terror seemed to subside as he spoke. "My suitcase..." his voice was weak and hoarse and he spaced out his words carefully, joltingly. " ...I can't carry it any more..." He wheezed again. "It's too heavy for me..."

"No problem!" Joaquin braced himself, placed his portfolio against the doorway, and stepped back across the hall. He felt saintly, magnanimous. He'd tell this one to Marina later and freak her out. Despite his smile, he was pretty scared, alright. Shocked, even. He kept a certain distance too — just do it and go. He picked up the suitcase and carried it into the elevator.

Then he waited, holding the heavy door open for several minutes as the man filed past him, slowly. When he'd shuffled over on a level with Joaquin's eyeline, he lifted his head without warning suddenly and caught him straight in the eyes. The confusing transmission was momentary, bolt-like: sweaty hospital beds, wires, tubes, nightmares, machines, drugs — prolonged and extreme struggle. Possibly what confused Joaquin most was a kind of edge, a frame that contained all of this, that was hard to define. An old-fashioned, biblical term whispered out from the back of his brain. It sounded something very like: courage.

He didn't look at the face again, but it filled his head as the guy turned around once inside the elevator, hunched and still clutching the woollen coat over his chest.

"Thank you . . ."

"Take care."

"God bless you."

The machinery screeched into motion as the elevator ascended, and the light went off in the hall. Joaquin stayed there in the darkness for a time, kicking his empty matchbox around the floor blindly. He finished his cigarette with unusual slowness before looking for the portfolio and heading out into the stifling day. He winced as he opened the door to the street, the light was blinding and the heat hit him like an oven blast. He felt distinctly sick, his hand shook visibly as he ran it over his forehead, and his features had fallen into the old nervous frown he'd spent so many years trying to get rid of. A small perspiration stain was already forming down the back of the grey shirt. He began to run suddenly, butting through the hoard of screaming kids outside the door. Dealers accosted him from doorways: "Smoke, Coke, Any high you want ..." Girls in large gold earrings conspired to push their prams in his path. He tore across Houston Street, barely missing a truck at the lights, incurring the wrath of its driver who roared at him coarsely in Creole.

A taxi — quick — the fastest possible conveyance to somewhere light-filled, clean and air-conditioned. He was going nuts, all the cabs seemed to be full. He tried hard to keep his mind on looking for one, on the encroaching interview. On what he would lie about on his resumé. On Marina. On anything. Only the day was tainted with the terrible stink of raw truth, like nothing he knew. Like the freakiness when lights dim subtly in a power surge, like the stereo just died at his party.

Park Avenue's flower-bordered luxury glided by outside, and by the time the cab passed fifty-seventh, Joaquin had almost managed to forget the face. Craig Overcash was still on the fucking radio, talking to a young prostitute who was baring her soul. Joaquin asked the driver to turn off the station, but he didn't speak English. So he sat there wondering how much a hired gun from Detroit would cost to take care of Craig...

"Yo! Carla honey, it sure is a jungle out there babe, and we thank you for sharing that with us... After the commercial break, coming up we have the latest on Madonna..." Music blared over the voice track, and as Joaquin spotted his destination coming up on the right he ordered the cab into the curb and took out his wallet. Sweet Mother of the devine Jesus, the one thing he just couldn't clear out of his head was that suitcase. A plain old bloody cardboard suitcase. It had been completely empty.

Colm O'Gaora

The Gunfighter

The two volunteers waited in silence. Occasionally one would look over at the other and catch a terror-struck eye. Even then no words of comfort or encouragement passed between them, just silence and the thick, clinging air of fear.

The narrow gravel road that separated them led into the city. On either side of it were large, rolling sand dunes, covered in thick clumps of marram grass. Odd items of rusting machinery lay half-submerged in the soft sand at the side of the road and it was behind these brown, sinking hulks that the volunteers lay waiting for the British Army patrol they knew would come this way.

They heard the crunch of the soldiers' jack-boots moments before the patrol came over the brow of a dune. The four soldiers marched two-abreast along the road with the sun screaming down upon the tender napes of their necks. The brass buttons on their tunics danced in the sunlight, spraying discs of shimmering light across the road. This did nothing to distract the attention of the two volunteers who had by now cocked their rifles and were sighting them upon those same sun-dancing brass buttons.

The reports of the first two shots were all but blown across the dunes by the breeze. Two of the soldiers heard only the curious, dull cracking and splintering of their colleagues' breast-bones as the lead bullets carved their way through bone and gristle. Instinctively, they dropped to the ground behind the two dead men. The volunteers waited a few moments until the third soldier lifted his rifle from his shoulder and looked up to take aim. A single bullet caught him high on the forehead and the impact momentarily lifted him into a kneeling position before his body slumped back to the ground. His colleague loosed off a volley of shots which ricocheted to safety along the centre of the road.

While the soldier re-loaded his rifle, Sean Hannan, the younger of the two volunteers, looked across at the other and smiled. Liam Curtin returned the smile, but signalled caution and patience before returning his gaze to a line along the barrel of his rifle. To his surprise a honey-bee had settled upon the gun-sight. He reached out and grabbed the bee with his hand. It beat frantically inside his fist, thumping tinily against his palms as he lifted it to his ear to listen to its buzz. The bee had distracted him and he let it go when he heard the sudden rasp of a foot on gravel. A shot punctured the stillness and he swung his rifle around to fire in the direction of the British soldier. He could hear the frantic sound of running alongside him and fired twice in rapid succession. The running stopped and Liam pressed his face into the sand, listening.

"Sean!" he called out after a few moments. "Sean!"

There was nothing; no answer, no sounds of movement. He looked up and saw that the body of the last British soldier lay face up in the middle of the road, his blind eyes staring at the passing clouds. Liam ran to where Sean lay crumpled in the gully at the side of the road. At first he thought the boy was only stunned but when he slapped his cheek Sean's head turned to reveal the gaping hole behind his ear. A dark crescent developed in the sand around his head; a halo of blood. Liam blessed himself and touched his fingers to the boy's lips. He leaned over and quickly prised Sean's fingers from the trigger of his gun. A good rifle was a valuable thing, and he could not leave it behind. Now there was another death to be avenged.

He crossed the road and pulled his bicycle from where he had hidden it in the shallow, soft sand. Leaping up on to the shiny leather saddle he glanced out over Dublin Bay, where a dark, rumbling thundercloud summoned its energy from the warm air.

I knew nothing of it then. He had telephoned me two nights before, asking me to come back to Ireland to see him. He wanted us all there, he said, he wanted us all to know. When I asked him to explain himself the line went dead. It was hardly surprising, coming from him. I walked to the open bedroom window and looked down at the street below. The neon sign over the door of the liquor store across from our block blinked twice and died. The last tram made its way along the centre of the avenue, flashes of blue where it caught the current from the overhead lines. Two dishevelled black men standing beneath a street-lamp shared a paper-wrapped bottle of bourbon. In the distance the skyscrapers stood emptied for the weekend, garlanded with cubes of light. The smell of warm charcoal came to me and I imagined that someone in an apartment below was putting out their grill. Around me the city groaned, cloaked in humidity, moisture suspended in the air. These were the sights and sounds of an American city and in the morning I would tell my wife, Anna, that for a few days I would forsake them to return to my grandfather's house in Dublin for no better reason other than he had asked me.

The city smelt faintly of the pavements which had been freshly sprinkled with rain from a passing thunderstorm. O'Connell Street was awash with its usual plethora of people set against a pastiche of garish shop-fronts; a collision of colour. Lilting voices, mothers scolding grubby, chocolate-stained children, greasy hand-prints on Clery's windows.

I found a taxi which swept me out along Mount Street towards the suburbs where I was born and where my grandfather now whittled his days away walking labradors on Sandymount Strand. The grotesque monotonous mortality of a man and his dogs set against a retreating tide; a life slipping away on a razor-shell-strewn beach; the marooned skull of an unfortunate Dalkey Island goat draped for death in seaweed, crabs for eyes.

Irene was at the house before me, heavy now with what would be my first nephew. Her awkward figure opened the door to me, the tendons flexing along her neck as she strained to kiss my cheek. The dogs yapped and barked at my feet, dribbling across my suitcase before deciding to follow me into the living-room where my grandfather languished at the fireside. The eyes in his balding, crenellate head turned to rest upon mine, a vivid red vein zig-zagging its way across the white of one eye.

"You are much too good to me, you know," he said, shifting his weight in the deep armchair. "I shouldn't have put any of you to all this trouble."

"No trouble at all, Pops," I replied. "No trouble at all. It's good to see you looking so well."

He exhaled loudly and phlegmatically through dry lips and turned his stare back towards the distorted reflection of himself to be found in the brass fireplace surround. He began muttering quietly to himself, indistinct words and syllables floating from his lips.

Irene tugged at my sleeve, beckoning me to come through to the kitchen. Following her I saw that the sideboard was laden with warm, buttered scones and freshly-baked brown bread.

"He has slipped since I last saw him at Christmas," I said. "His spirit seems to have gone."

"He has had it bad with his chest since March. Between the emphysema and the damp weather he's had a hard time of it."

I looked around at the kitchen Irene had kept scrupulously clean. His trademarks were gone: the row of old pipes in the dresser, the small pot-cacti ranged along the windowsill, his boots standing beside the back door. He was being edged out slowly.

"He hardly had a word for me," I said.

"He has little to say to any of us these days, very little at all." She whisked her hand around the water in the sink, retrieving potato peelings which she dumped in the bin at her feet. "I just leave him be."

"You can't ignore him, Irene."

"I *don't* ignore him." She turned away from the sink and looked at me, water dripping from her reddened hands. "*You* don't have to live with him."

I felt uncomfortable for having questioned how she coped with him. It was true: I was at the periphery of the family now, with my American wife and sons. I had removed myself from Liam's shadow.

A few minutes later she laid a mug of tea on the table in front of me. I thanked her for it and went to sit in the old rocking-chair at the window. "Have you any idea why he wanted me to come all this way? He said he wanted us to know something. What?"

"I wish I knew, Eamonn, I really wish I knew,"she said.

"I suppose we'll get some sort of an explanation at dinner tomorrow night. Siobhan can't come until then, so we'll hear nothing from him in the meantime."

I turned to look out through the window at the garden. It looked so bedraggled now; Irene's sphere of influence had clearly not extended as far as the garden. The hedges were overgrown, the flower-beds bare, the roses pruned back into crude black stumps. The sundial that stood in the centre of the lawn was now overrun with creeping ivy. No shadow had been cast upon its brass face for years. I remembered the days when all his hours were spent out there, tending to the climbing plants, the rockeries, the lawn, the shrubbery. Invariably there had been casualties: the prize *clematis montana* frozen to the downpipe the year that my parents were killed, the wallflowers crushed and petrified by a late fall of snow, the sleeping hedgehogs dragged out to die from exposure by labrador puppies. This year, no stinging frosts, no snow, ageing labradors. No casualties yet.

Looking out at the state of the garden made me impatient with Irene and her smug school-teacher husband.

"Will you ever get around to mowing the lawn this year?" I said. "Just for his sake, of course."

There was no reply. I turned around. Irene had slipped out while I had my back turned and the room was suddenly, violently empty. I felt uncomfortable in a room I had grown up in. I emptied the dregs of the milky tea into the sink.

Wandering back into the living room I noticed that the old man was sleeping his troubled sleep. From time to time his hand would lift from the arm-rest as if he were about to say something and an expression would form upon his face; then his arm would drop and the expression fade. His hollow, aching wheeze blended with the roar the flames made in the hearth as they escaped up the chimney.

Little had changed in this room since the days when I had spent my evenings here poring over school exercises and the leather-bound collections of Shakespeare and Homer which still stood upon the bookshelves in the alcoves at either side of the hearth. The deep-green flock wallpaper had survived intact. At times it lent the room the look of a fifties hotel lounge, with its large oak furniture and the lavishly upholstered *chaise-longue* beneath the window.

In the far corner the gun cabinet stood like a sentinel. The leaded glass in its doors was as clear as crystal and cast my reflection back at me in a bluish haze. The large brass lock caught the lamplight and sent it in a shaft to the floor where it formed a dull puddle of liquid gold. When I opened the cabinet door the beam of light shifted and bounced off a mirror-topped coffee table and thence on to the crown of my grandfather's head. Intrigued, I watched it flicker there for a moment before looking into the dark interior of the cabinet. The acrid odour of metal polish mingled with the smell of leather filling my nostrils. Clearly, the old man had not neglected the rifles which had stood here since the Civil War had ended in the early 1920's. Indeed, it smelled as if they had been polished that very day. It was hardly likely.

From the fireside came a sudden, rasping cough. A gob of the old man's phlegm hit the fire-grate with a loud hiss. He mumbled a little and the arm-chair creaked while he settled back into it.

By the time I had returned to the kitchen Irene had fed the dogs. They dozed in a gloomy corner of the room.

"You must be tired after the long flight over," she said, squeezing a floor-cloth between her hands. "The jet-lag always catches up on you."

A wave of warm lethargy spread through me as I nodded agreement with her. I wished her goodnight.

"You're in your old room tonight," she called up the stairs after I had gone.

I lay in bed staring at the ceiling rose for longer than I wished. I was remembering my grandfather as I had known him as a child; as I had known him before I had grown to know too much. I remembered particularly how I had found him on the beach that August morning: standing still, naked, up to his knees in water, his eyes fixed upon a vanishing point in the distance, his heart set elsewhere. His brown jacket and trousers rolled in the foam at the edge of the surf. His shoes had already filled with sand. He had been standing there for some time, hesitating, caught between one life, one reality, and another he wished for.

"Pops! Pops!" I shouted, stepping high through the fizzing waves. He did not run but bowed his head.

"Are you going for a swim?" I asked when I caught up with him.

He cupped his hands over his groin, like I had seen footballers do.

"Look," he said simply, indicating with a nod the sea in front of us.

I looked. A series of sleek black humps broke through the water no more than a hundred yards away from us. They moved steadily across the bay.

"Porpoises," he said, and we looked a little longer. I felt his hand heavy upon the crown of my head. It trembled.

As we walked back through the water, gathering his drowned clothes, reclaiming the shoes, he stopped for a moment. I looked back at him, twisting his tie between his fingers.

"Someday you'll learn to forgive your grandad!"

His words made no sense to me, but even then I sensed their importance and did not question him again. Instead, I tried to take my eyes from his exposed groin, but could not resist that childhood fascination.

Other moments in time slowly returned to me one after another, indexed as always by the internal music I invariably tagged to these stills of life: the fizz and bubble of the waves on a Connemara beach that morning as we stood entranced by a school of porpoises, the suck-plop of the peat bog from which my parent's car was pulled on a cold, misty October evening, the rattle of pebbles hitting coffin lids while their double grave was filled in, the insistent humming of the cardiac monitor attached to their driver as he lay on a hospital bed for days afterwards. Then, he talked only of his dogs.

Siobhan, the younger of my two sisters, arrived at noon the following day. She too had travelled some considerable distance in answer to a call from her grandfather. London had been good to her and she was now an associate in a Holborn advertising agency. She had booked herself into a plush hotel in Ballsbridge for the few days she intended spending in Dublin

"Hey, big brother!" It was her usual greeting. She had not lost many of her teenage habits and nuances. They were at once irritating and endearing. "What's with the old man now?"

"Don't ask," said Irene. "Come into the kitchen for some tea. You're looking well."

While they chatted in the kitchen I stood in the hallway examining the photographs ranged along its walls. There was just one photograph of my parents, taken in the Botanic Gardens in Glasnevin during their last summer. My mother wore a long flowing pale dress and held a wide-brimmed hat on her head with one hand. Her chin was lifted up a little as she peered at the camera. My father stood beside her, feet apart, his hands pushed into the pockets of his trousers. His dark hair was oiled back and beneath the pronounced eyebrows I had inherited from him, his hazel eyes stared hard into the lens.

I looked at the photograph more closely and noticed that at the edge of the print, beside my father, ran a narrow fraction of someone else's arm. Below that could be seen the edge of a shoe. It could have been no-one else but my grandfather. Someone had cropped the print so that he would not appear alongside my parents in the last photograph taken of them before they died. And yet, when I stepped back and looked at it again, those blurred pieces of sleeve and shoe were all that I could see.

Later, Siobhan and I exchanged news as we set out the table for the meal Irene had cooked for the four of us. I threw more coal on the fire and uncorked the wine. Together the three of us ferried the food from the kitchen to the dining table.

"Come on, Pops" said Siobhan, "you'll burn up if you sit at that fire any longer." She helped him up out of the armchair while Irene pulled a chair out from the head of the table for him. When he had sat down she hung his stick on the back of the chair. His hands gripped the arm-rests as he leaned forward to look at us.

"Nice to see us all here, eating at the same table again," he said, picking up his soup spoon.

"It's not *that* long since we were here last," Siobhan commented.

He stirred the consommé with the spoon, blowing upon its surface to cool it down. The sound was that of a hoarse half-whisper as the air whistled around his loose dentures. Siobhan stared at him intently, a spoonful of soup suspended halfway between her bowl and her mouth. I glanced across at Irene, whose face seemed set, unperturbed. The whistling sound died down as he ran out of breath. Siobhan sighed and took her first spoonful of soup. I watched as he lifted the full spoonful to his lips and at the last moment noticed that Irene was wincing.

The gurgling, flooding sound that followed caused Siobhan to drop her spoon into her bowl. Irene was still wincing, and her shoulders shook a little. I noticed that as he ate his eyes were closed and his face took on an expression of ecstasy and anticipation: the face of a child being given a sweet cough mixture. Much of the soup spilled back out of his mouth and into his bowl or down his chin. As he breathed out after each swallow, droplets of consommé leapt from his lips into the air. I could not be sure that Irene hadn't planned it this way: serving soup to demonstrate how difficult he had made life for her and that Siobhan and I should be grateful to her for taking him on.

"So little has changed since we had dinner at this table every Sunday evening years ago," I said as soon as he had finished his soup. I hoped to dispel the atmosphere that his soup-eating had fostered. After a silence it was he that spoke.

"That's true, Eamonn. It's a pity the chance won't come around again".

"Don't be daft!" Irene exclaimed. "We'll all be here again at Christmas, won't we?" She looked at Siobhan and I.

"Not" I thought, "if we're going to have soup again."

Siobhan remained silent, looking into space. I imagined that at that moment she wanted desperately to be back in London, to be away from us all, away from the grandfather who disgusted her so much.

"Won't we?" Irene repeated, louder this time.

I nodded. Siobhan woke from her day-dream and agreed.

"I think this chest of mine will get the better of me before then," Pops said, adding a violent cough to emphasise his point.

"Nonsense," said Irene, picking the empty soup bowls off the table and bringing them back to the kitchen.

While Irene filled our plates with meat and vegetables we talked about Siobhan's career and the changes in the school curriculum which meant that Irene's husband had had to change schools. Although we tried to engage him in conversation Pops would not talk.

When he went to cut his meat the knife wobbled between his fingers and then, as he ate, most of the food fell from the fork on to his plate. He chewed the tiny morsels with exaggerated effort and Siobhan kept her eyes upon her own plate and the label on the wine bottle in front of her.

"This talk of your chest getting you down is rubbish, and I won't hear of it," said Irene. "The Black and Tans couldn't nail you during the Civil War and it'll take more than a bad cough to get you down for too long."

I leaned across to top up his glass in encouragement even though he had not touched his wine. He poked wearily at his food, clearly not wanting to eat but not wishing to offend Irene either.

"I have neither the spirit nor the will now that I had then," he said, and after a time he added, "I'm a different man now."

"Listen, Pops" Irene began, "don't start trading sympathies with us. You spent enough time talking about the Civil War to convince us you were a one-man army. You have a reputation to live up to now." She smiled, clearly hoping that the jibe would humour him.

He scowled. A lump of half-chewed beef rolled off his bottom lip and dropped into his plate. "I've a different mind on all that now." He turned his head to cough. "I can't rely on memories to keep the dream alive. Look at the state of The North now! A bloody mess is what it is!" He began to cough loudly and I patted his back as his face reddened. "I should have buried the memories long ago," he continued after a while. "It's the ramblings of people like me that have created the myth that those thugs in The North live by. They look on the likes of me as heroes, patriots. I'm what has the place the way it is."

"There's no need for any of that, Pops" I said, "what's done is done. You did what was right at the time."

"It's not done, Eamonn, it's not done yet. It's still going on up there, and the fact that I did it sixty years ago makes me no different from the lot of them. They say that it was us that brought about the Republic. Huh! All those deaths, executions, widows and orphans. And for what? A freedom achieved years afterwards of its own will. It would have happened anyway, without the likes of me murdering Englishmen." He set his cutlery down on the edge of his plate with a soft clink. "Or Irishmen for that matter."

The room was suddenly enveloped in a thick silence that was hardly silence at all. Each of us was looking for a way out of it. We stopped eating, stopped chewing. Siobhan swallowed hard and although she stared at the wine label even more intently than before, I knew that she too was listening out. Irene brushed the palms of her hands with a napkin, her mouth set fast, her lips bunched together. Darkness stood outside the window behind his head, twitching with curiosity. Moths streaked through it.

In the end it was he that defused it: "I am thinking of young Sean Hannan. Seventeen he was, seventeen." He paused to sigh.

His sombre tone was infectious, viral — darkness seemed to creep in and take its place at our table. "I am thinking of him now, thinking of the family he would have had and the lives they too would have lived."

"Well!" Irene interrupted, "I have never heard such rubbish coming from a grown man in all my born days!"

Pops ignored her and continued in the same sad, prosaic tone as before: "I am thinking of the day that he died. Is it really sixty years? It was a day not unlike this one, you know. Dull, cloudy; thunderstorms rolling around the sky like demented ghosts. He should have lived to see another day — not I." He coughed, turning away from the table to cup a hand over his mouth. I caught the gleam of a tear gathering in the corner of his eye.

Irene took the opportunity to interrupt again. "Sean Hannan was killed by a British bullet and that's all there is to it. Sure isn't that his rifle in the cabinet over there along with your own?"

We looked over at the cabinet while he drew a long breath. I felt his hand upon my forearm. He tightened his grip and asked me: "Will you fetch me his rifle?"

Under protest from Irene I took the rifle from its resting-place and brought it to him. He took it in his gnarled hands, running a finger along the smooth length of the barrel.

Examining it, he said, "I am tired of thinking of him now, tired of being like this. Those thoughts have me trapped now, locked away by what might and could have been. It should have been me really, lying at the side of the road that morning."

"We understand how you must feel" Siobhan said calmly, "but there's no need to burden yourself with blame at this stage. No-one else blames you."

"No-one else knows the truth, that's why." He shifted the rifle from one hand to the other.

I looked at my sisters and then turned my gaze towards him.

"Don't any of you see what I'm trying to say?" His voice faltered. "I..."

"Now, now, Pops" said Irene, "that's no way to be acting on a night like this. Just forget about the whole thing. Eat your dinner and be thankful for the life you have got. And would you ever put away that monstrosity of a gun — it's making me nervous."

"Let him say what he has to say," I snapped. I tapped his shoulder. "Go on, Pops."

He looked at me and I could see that he was grateful for the opportunity to talk without interruption. He quivered with nerves and faltered on his first words. "F... Forgive me for all this trouble, calling you over here. It wasn't without good reason." He leaned forward and propped his head up with his hand at his temple. His fingers were long and liver-mottled against his forehead. His eyes were fixed upon the carpet at his feet, as if he was concentrating upon words coming from far away. "I regret...no... I have never forgiven myself for your parents' death. I lost more than a son and daughter-in-law in the crash. It was an accident, you know that. But I had my mind on other things as we drove back from the hotel that night. I was thinking of the laughs we had had at the party and your mother was re-telling some of the stories we had heard. The three of us were laughing away — until I caught sight of myself in the rear-view mirror." He lifted his head for a moment and looked at us before continuing. "I saw myself smiling away without a care in the world, laughing with your parents, happy to be there. And then I thought of that young boy who could not be there — that young boy whose absence from the world is my fault."

His elbow slid forward across the table and his head dropped towards the polished teak surface. I grabbed his wrist and pulled him upright. I could hear Irene and Siobhan cursing behind me. He grabbed my elbows and drew himself upright with sudden strength. Pushing his face close to mine I could smell the sourness in his breath.

"I killed him, by God! I killed the poor boy. He got in the way and I killed him." He was frantic now, grabbing for my clothes, trying to pull me close. A wine glass toppled over and sent its contents splashing across the table-cloth. I steadied him, his words racing through my mind as I worked to comprehend them.

Quite suddenly he pulled the rifle to him. The muzzle fell against the leathery skin of his neck and he leaned down upon it. His face was fixed in concentration and determination to finish what he had obviously set out to do. My sisters screamed and the whole room seemed to reach out towards him, to pull the rifle away as time slowed to an impossible pace.

He needed both hands to pull the trigger. He clenched his eyes shut and breathed in. There was a solid, deadly click as he pulled. At first there was no report and his face in that astonishing moment was almost comical: his re-opened eyes above puffed-out cheeks; startled and surprised, like a trumpeter whose instrument has dissolved in his hands.

The loud crack of the report caused the crockery to jump upon the table. The wine glasses shattered, spilling wine across our laps. The bullet exited through the crown of his head and lodged in the ceiling. Splinters of plaster scattered across our heads, resting in the eyebrows above his unseeing eyes. There were pin-pricks of his blood upon our faces.

As I leaned helplessly over his body I looked up at the window. The moths were hysterical now, blurring together in the pitch blackness, struggling for the light, desperate. And he too, the dead man I now held by the shoulders, had been desperate. Desperate for forgiveness, desperate to be freed from the memories that had stayed with him every hour of every day since, every second of a lifetime.

Harry Clifton

From

A Ship Came from Valparaiso

The time is 1981, the place Aranyaprathet, on the border between Thailand and Cambodia, around which are clustered refugee camps, official or otherwise. The narrator, a minor Irish diplomat, and his boon companion Luke Fortune, drive north on a business visit to these camps.

Two more years had gone by.

We were travelling north, from Trat to Aranyaprathet, in the limousine Gavin Stockwell had comandeered for his official duties. The Mud Bomber, he had baptised it, for the flooded refugee camps it had splashed him through in monsoon season. He had needed it in his early days there as an engineering supervisor, when the camps were mud and chaos, children on their last legs from the border crossing into Thailand and international television crews snarled in their own wires. I had seen the footage back in Dublin, at the height of the crisis. Gavin Stockwell's face, earnest, humanitarian, troubled, repeating the rhetoric of our glasstopped table days into half the screens of Ireland. A masterly political stroke. You had to admire the man, really. Strictly speaking, though, the Mud Bomber should long since have reverted to the car pool, since Gavin Stockwell had moved from the field to administration. But by the time I was posted there a year later, he still had it. And we would have it to the end, he assured me, for only a few months remained to either of us in the country. Such was his prestige he had even retained his driver, an alcoholic named Somchat who ran a prostitution racket in his free hours. With Somchat at the wheel, the Mud Bomber was carrying us north, on official business.

"The old Chinaman," Gavin Stockwell said.

"What do we do about him?"

"Put him on a bus," I said. "Send him south to our camp. We'll deal with him there."

The old Chinaman was one of our little embarrassments. Even God, if he existed, would have little embarrassments. At that point in our existence, we were as near to being God as you can imagine on this earth, in the late bureaucratic age. But it is one thing to hold sway over the lives of a hundred thousand Cambodians, of fifty thousand Laotians, even of a hundred Vietnamese awkward customers caught up in the wheels of history, all clamouring for resettlement in the New World. These can be reduced to immigration quotas, official policies. But an old Chinaman — an individual! — now there is a spanner in the works. There is no precedent. Statistics don't fit. The Chinese Embassy is taking an interest in the case. Then, by God, you open the rulebook with trembling hands, and prove your worth as a bureaucrat.

"If not conscience," I added, invoking my favourite motto, "at least conscientiousness."

But Gavin Stockwell had already lost interest. He was the image man, the dirty work was down to me. Peace-ful Ea-sy Fee-ling, he was humming, along with the tape of soft Californian rock that Somchat had plugged into the dashboard. His mind was on higher things, like Reaganite economics and his own political career back in Ireland. Power, the taste of power he had had out here, had made him avuncular, prematurely middleaged. He had grown a beard, developed a pot belly, satiated his lusts with local women. Peace-ful Ea-sy Fee-ling, the tape pounded, like the blood softly pounding in my head, oxygenated by the airconditioning system in the closed limousine. The rippling green paddyfields, the temples that seemed to float in skyblue water — as far as I was concerned, they were all just another province of the American Middle West.

"You,"said Gavin Stockwell, "where will they post you next?"

"The ambassador was through from India last week," I said. "He told me I'd served my time in the tropics. First Africa, now this. I'm putting in for New York."

"I hear he has a gorgeous South American wife," said Gavin Stockwell.

"They're getting divorced. The children are in boarding school in Switzerland."

"That's the diplomatic life. Stay loose, play the field."

We entered the outskirts of Aranyaprathet. Red Cross depots. Compounds beaten to a shiny flatness by the marching and countermarching of soldiers. We passed them, the jogging and chanting platoons, sweating, stripped to their singlets, on the open road. Army lorries veered crazily past us in the opposite direction, carrying tailboards of drunken soldiers away from border duty to their families in the Bangkok slums. Already I smelled the border, on the other side of Aranyaprathet. A no-man's land, filled with people of undefined status. I didn't like people of undefined status, zones that belonged to god knows whom, boundaries that shifted every few weeks. They offended my sense of order, they made hash out of my filing system. I wanted the old Chinaman out of there and down south, where I could control things better.

"Let's go straight through to the camp," Gavin Stockwell said. "We can do our business there this afternoon, and enjoy ourselves in town tonight."

No man's land, in early afternoon, was a blast of heat. In the shell craters, dead water buffalo floated, in their own green scum. The Mud Bomber bounced on its shock absorbers, its windscreen caked with red dust as it roared along the dirt track through featureless scrubland sandbagged with gun emplacements. We came to a checkpoint, the sawnoff branch of a tree flung across the track. Baby faced soldiers in milky reflecting sunglasses advanced upon us and took away our passes. Not that the passes mattered. Everything was unofficial anyway, with the deadly complicity of the great powers — the traffic in contraband and ruined lives, the illegals roasting all day for punishment inside a circle of barbed wire by the checkpoint. An electricity sang in the air, higher than the sizzle of heat and cicadas — the electricity of pure politics. In the glasses of the baby faced soldeirs, as they handed back our passes, I saw myself reflected. An unpleasant realisation. Politically, I preferred abstraction to the suppurating smell of reality.

As we passed through the checkpoint, a band of refugees filed along the track towards us. On their shoulders they were carrying a huge dead boa constrictor with a gorgeous skin.

"That's worth a fortune," Gavin Stockwell said. "They could barter themselves halfway to America with that skin. I know a doctor who'd have bought it. Except she's been deported already for smuggling stuff out of the camps."

Behind us on the carseat, a radio with a whiplash antenna blurted into life. We had entered the electromagnetic field of the border camps. The voices of agency personnel, nurses calling for aid, drivers bogged to the axles in mud, floated, disembodied, in the pure ether of their condition. They sounded lost and plaintive, like confused angels or the souls of the recently dead, trying to orient themselves in a new and terrible afterlife. I belonged to that afterlife, so did Gavin Stockwell. Irritatedly he reached behind him and switched off the receiver.

"Bad cess to them!" he muttered. "Do they think I'm here to solve their problems? As if a year in this camp wasn't enough for me..."

Actually, cesspools were what had brought Gavin Stockwell north on this occasion, much against his will. His little embarrassment, so to speak. For the sewage system he had devised a year previously had proved woefully inadequate. It was in the wrong soil, the water table was too near the surface — in short, it had flooded. Though a master of his humanitarian image, when it came to engineering realities Gavin Stockwell was, unfortunately, the son of his father. But he had enough of his mother in him to wrap a clean white sweat-towel around his neck, bring along his camera, and hope for a photo-opportunity. Somchat too, alive to the possibilities in the situation, had unloaded two suitcases for contraband from the boot of the Mud Bomber. United in our ideals, the three of us set off together.

The camp was laid out on the grid system of an American city. A rough imitation, obviously, for the buildings and streets were alleys of rat-infested bamboo hovels roofed with straw, crowded with armless, legless destitute victims of carpet bombings and other strategic necessities. But the aspiration was there, that was the main thing. So the streets bore the names of American presidents. Richard Nixon Street, for instance, was where the camp brothel was located — a corrugated iron structure, with military motorbikes drawn up outside, busy even at this hour. Distressingly, it was John Fitzgerald Kennedy Street where the sewers had erupted, right under an anonymous building we all knew as the C.I.A. recruitment centre. An overpowering excremental stench emanated from it. Piles of shitstained official documents had been moved to huts commandeered on either side. As a bureaucrat myself, I could sympathise with the problems involved in cleaning up that mess. I left Gavin Stockwell and Somchat there, berating the camp foreman, and proceeded on my way. My own business was on Ronald Reagan Avenue.

The old Chinaman lived at Number Six. Hut Number Six, that is. Hut Number Seven, adjoining it, he had converted to a small school, where he taught English to refugee children. His own English he had learned from American forces in China, during the Second World War. Later, his children had emigrated there, and now, a wandering old man caught up in the Indochinese firestorm, he aspired to follow them there. To die with what was left of his family, I seem to remember him saying. His personal concerns were his own business, not mine. I heard the light, regular chanting of children at lessons as I approached Number Seven. When my shadow fell across the doorway there was a pause, before they stood respectfully to attention.

"Where there has been misfortune," the old Chinaman said, "children need order, a clean space for beauty and the spirit."

I followed him next door to Number Six. Like the school, it was a miracle of cleanliness in the squalor that was Ronald Reagan Avenue. There was a waterbutt and a sack of rice in opposite corners, between which was a swept floorspace. The sleeping mats for himself and his greyhaired wife stood folded against the wall. There were books on improvised shelves, and overlooking everything, a Buddhist shrine smoking with lit incense sticks. I refused the tea his wife had made, but accepted the beautifully crafted razor he offered me as a present. In return, I presented him with the document of a lifetime. Twenty-five clauses, each beginning with the word "whereas", each letting me off the hook in the event of some contingency, terminating in a short statement to the effect that he had official status now, he was no longer a nobody, the West had him on its books.

"Don't try to understand it," I told him. "Just give it to the camp commander. You're going south with the next consignment."

To my annoyance, he was largely unmoved. It is not every day a god descends into your realm to raise you to the next level nearer the American paradise you aspire towards. But I wasn't in the mood to stay around and wait for the prostrate thanks that was my due, so we shook hands quickly and I left it at that. When I got back to the Mud Bomber, Gavin Stockwell and Somchat were already waiting.

"I wiped the foreman's face," Gavin Stockwell said happily, "with John Fitzgerald Kennedy's shit."

Somchat let out a burst of high, hysterical laughter, totally without humour. Pure nerves. As we drove away, I wondered what the Mud Bomber was carrying in its boot. Blackmarket gold? Tetracycline? Best quality Laotian weed? Only when the baby faced soldiers had waved us through the checkpoint did he begin to relax. He had a woman in Aranyaprathet, we both knew, he would stay with her tonight. In the front seat, Gavin Stockwell shot him a glance of warm fatherly solicitude.

"Life with us is good, isn't it?" he said.

That evening, when we had cleaned the camp dust off ourselves, we went to eat under the flourescent striplights of the market place. Aranyaprathet had come alive after dark. It swarmed with motorbikes driven by youths in Hawaiian beachshirts, their blackhaired girlfriends clinging, sitting sideways on the pillion.

"Don't you feel you're part of an old movie here sometimes?" Gavin Stockwell suggested.

"A movie set in America," I said, "in the 1950s." Halfheartedly, I dipped a prawn into hot sauce and took a slug of beer. I preferred the Hamburger Saloon, which Gavin Stockwell had helped set up the previous year, and which had recently been the object of an incendiary attack. Its blackened remains stood between a house showing art movies and a massage parlour.

"There goes the camp heart throb," said Gavin Stockwell.

A handsome man in a floppy white hat emerged from the massage parlour, on the arm of a young Thai woman known to me only by her working name of Apple. She raised two fingers at us as the pair of them swayed down the road to the bar.

"He's moving to El Salvador," Gavin Stockwell sneered, "where the media have gone. It's not SEXY to be in Thailand anymore."

I sensed that Gavin Stockwell was less than happy to be back in his old stamping ground. But against our better judgement, we followed the other two down to the bar. Really just a light burning above a door in a wall. There were jeeps, limousines and trucks parked for fifty yards on either side — the traffic of the camps and military installations. A bevy of girls whose faces wore the garish masks of their profession bade us enter, pushing the door wide.

"This is where the grenade was thrown last month," Gavin Stockwell said nervously. "There were six killed in here."

Inside, though the ceiling was held up with scaffolding, it was business as usual. Emotionless, efficient, a blankfaced oriental band played western favourites from the sixties, while a small crowd danced in the hot light in front of the stage. I recognised the camp heart-throb dancing with Apple, and among the seated listeners many tired habituees who had stayed on in the camps after the first crisis, when the glamour had passed. Through a miasma of toxins, they regarded Gavin Stockwell, their former colleague, with bleary jaundiced eyes.

"Who's shovelling the shit on JFK Street these days?" one of them asked, to general laughter.

"Is it my fault if I was promoted," Gavin Stockwell said testily, "and the rest of you weren't?"

"That's what promotion means," the other went on.

"They give you a bigger shovel."

"Admittedly it's not very photogenic," another butted in, "shovelling shit. Metro Goldwyn Meyer mightn't be interested."

"I've had enough of this," Gavin Stockwell said, making for the door.

But worse was to follow. Before he had made it outside, Apple intercepted him from the dancefloor. In a single fluent and entirely unexpected gesture, she reached up as if to kiss him and emitted from her mouth a bile yellow stream that ran down his face and clung to his beard and shirtfront. After a moment of stunned silence, during which it became clear the bar was on her side, not ours, Gavin Stockwell decided against reacting in his normal fashion. She followed up with a contemptuous gob of spittle and stalked back to the dance floor.

"The last time I had that one," he said to me bitterly as we walked away into the night, "I left her bleeding from her back passage..."

Sara Berkeley

From

The Swimmer
in the
Deep Blue Dream

*Camilla, the narrator of this novella, has left university and her
family in Dublin, bringing a dark secret with her, and gone to find
work in London, where she moved in with her bachelor uncle,
Hugh.*

One evening there was a call from a boy I'd known at home. He
was passing through London, he said. Could he stay one night,
and he'd be on the plane at eleven the next day. John Curie was
a friend I'd made in college and when I thought about seeing him,
I was glad. He was a skinny, serious guy with a lot of energy,
which he often expanded in long intense arguments about
whatever topic took his fancy.

"Are you out of college then?" I said, but as I did, I could hear
the pips of a public phone.

"No more money! "he shouted. "See you Thursday!"

John arrived in a welter of disorganised luggage. I met him at
the station and he hugged me with unexpected warmth.

"Jesus I'd to leg it for my plane," he said. "They kept the doors
open for me while they taxied down the runway. Heathrow's a
desperate place. And fuckin miles away. What possesses your
uncle to live out here?"

He kept it up till we reached the house, a stream of anecdotes and funny stories about the journey. It wasn't until we were at the garden gate that I asked where he was off to.

"Australia," he said shortly, and we stopped, facing each other, our hands on the gate. "I'm getting out."

"For good?" I asked, expecting him to say "Well, for a year anyway, to see what it's like."

But he raised his eyebrows and dropped them quickly.

"Fuckin right," he said.

Over dinner John told me and Hugh stories: about people I'd known, and things that happened in college, parties and fights and resits, and the nights before resits, and the nights after. He kept us laughing and after a while, Hugh began to remember his own college days in London in the late sixties. Soon he had us crying with laughter, and we carried on long after the meal was over, until Hugh pushed his chair back and said "Will we go for a drink."

It was the first time since I'd come that we'd been to the local pub. It was full, people spilling out on the pavements, and Hugh said there was another he knew that would be quieter.

"This is where I used to go with your father," he said, leading us into a smaller pub with a wooden floor and wooden benches.

"This is grand," John said, and ordered drinks. When he brought them back to the table I proposed a toast to Australia.

"Yeah," he said darkly, and we drank for a while in a sudden gloom.

"Did you get a visa," I said.

"It's all organised."

"Do you know people there?"

"Eddie's out there. And Anus."

"Anus?" said Hugh.

"His real name's Fergus," I explained. "But he's a bit of a, y'know."

"Oh," said Hugh.

John changed the subject then and we didn't refer to Australia again until after the third or fourth round, when Hugh got up to leave.

"Aged Uncle Reels Home In Alcoholic Haze" he said, and we wished him goodnight.

"Your uncle's great."

"Yeah. I hardly knew him before, but we really get on."

"He's let me stay there, now he says I can stay for as long as I want."

"How long's that."

"I don't know," I said firmly.

"What are you up to, Cam?"

"What do you mean, up to?"

"You were always a dark horse. There's lots going on there, isn't there," he nodded towards my head.

"Too much sometimes."

"What are you doing in a fuckin typing job."

"Typing." The coolness of my answer shut him up for a bit. But he wasn't letting go.

"Why did you leave college like that?"

"I wanted to."

"Before the exams? Jesus, Cam. You would've done brilliant."

I said nothing. The alcohol was working and I didn't trust the looseness I could feel, the rising sense of recklessness.

"Did something happen?"

He was looking at me seriously. There didn't seem any point lying, like there always had been.

"I don't want to talk about it."

"Cam. I'm a dead man."

"What?" I wondered for a moment if he was in trouble with the police.

"You know. Remember in the famine when the ships left for America they'd have an American wake the night before."

"Ah John!"

"I mean it," he leaned forward, suddenly aggressive. "They're dead people back there, all of them, and I'm a dead man. It all starts tomorrow at eleven when I step on that plane."

"So I'm dead too."

"No." He sat back. "You're not dead." Finishing his drink, he got up to go to the bar. "You're just asleep."

He smiled down at me then and something indefinable was exchanged in the look. A sense of boundless possibility swept over me as I watched him at the bar. I thought fleetingly of standing beside him, with his arm round me. Then another picture blotted this out, and I got up abruptly from the table and hurried to the bathroom as though a giant bat had folded its clammy wings around me and I had to break free.

We drank till closing time, and John attempted to convince me I should come to Australia. There were jobs there, there was sun and sea and endless tracts of empty land. Imagine the outback, he said. You could go out there and just get lost for a month. And the dance parties. He'd heard about them, in Sydney, where twenty thousand people threw a party on the wharves and just danced and drank and got high for a whole weekend. Imagine it, Cam, he said. And I imagined. "You'd love it," he said, and I shook my head.

"Look," he said, and laid both hands flat on the table. "You're not going back home, right? And you're not going back to college. You're sitting here telling me you want to stay in London and type. You're four times brighter than I ever was."

"That's not true, you just didn't work."

"You're still a bright girl Cam, and you're wasting your time."

I felt the unfairness of it building up inside. "It's not that," I said hopelessly. The pub was emptying. People were drinking up. A barman came to wipe our table. "Let's go back."

Outside the pub he slipped his arm around me, natural as water. "Let's walk," he said.

"No," I said. "Hugh will be asleep. Let's go back and make coffee and scoff some biscuits."

We let ourselves in, giggling a little at the state of Hugh's garden, and made some coffee in the kitchen without switching the light on.

"Let's see if we can locate the sugar," John said, fumbling around the packets and bins in Hugh's cupboard. We spoke in exaggerated whispers and it seemed tremendously funny every time one of us knocked something over. We carried the coffee, spilling some, out into the hall. But instead of going into the back room, I chose the front. This room was as bland as any unused parlour in a fifties house. There was flock wallpaper and a hideous fireplace. We stood in the middle of the room, taking in the curtains and the fake paintings, and I said "This is sad" and we started to laugh and couldn't stop.

"What the fuck's this?" John held up a plastic vase with a single plastic flower. I exploded with fresh laughter.

"It must have been my granny's. Aw, look at this!" I picked up an ancient magazine rack in the shape of a swan. There was a Daily Mirror from 1989. "I can't believe this! Hugh must never come in here."

"The Room That Time Forgot," said John in a deep voice.

More suppressed laughter. We sobered up a little then and sat side by side on the couch, reading the unlikely news of March 28th 1989. We read our horoscopes, and decided what we'd watch on telly. We started the crossword, then gave up because neither of us wanted to fetch a pen. I lay back on the couch with my legs across John's lap.

"So tell me," he said, and then stared into his coffee cup for a while. "You couldn't take the pace or something. Was that it?"

"It pissed me off," I said, "going in there, taking classes, writing essays. What could I do at the end of it?"

"More than type," he said, barely audibly.

"I'll get a better job," I said, but he shook his head.

"I don't understand you." He was playing with the buckle on my shoes, pulling at it and letting it go. "I never understood you. Great crack to be with, but one move and you clammed up."

I let my head drop back on the armrest so he couldn't see my face very well. It was as though he had me trapped there, gently trapped, like an animal he was holding firmly by the paw.

"Will you sleep with me?"

"No."

"Once. The night before I go, huh? One last night."

"No John."

"Your uncle won't know."

"It's not my uncle."

"Have you ever before?"

"This isn't questions and answers time, John." The blood pumped slower, somehow, with my head at this angle. It rose with effort to the brain and I felt that racy feeling from too little oxygen, that quickening before you take a high dive.

"There's no need to be ashamed of that. I think it's nice."

"You don't know. You don't know what you're talking about. I'm not a virgin." I stopped on the brink. You could dive from here and you might be dead before you touched the water. "Now leave the subject alone." There was a deathly tone of authority in my voice that surprised me.

John said nothing for a time. Then I felt him circle my right ankle with his fingers. They just met. "I really like you, Cam. If there's something that's happened to you and you think it would help to say it to someone you'll probably never see again, go ahead. I won't be seeing anyone who'll need to know."

Say it then, Cam. Just say the words. Just see what they sound like, hanging in the room here for a while, then going away. Would they go away? They might always be here then, like a murderer's bloody hands, veined and terrible. They are bigger, those words than this room. Bigger than the house, than London, than the whole of Australia. They're too big for me, and too big for Rene. They sent me away, and I haven't gone far enough."

"Maybe," I said, "I'll follow you out."

I woke early, to sudden, sharp jabs of panic. I lay, not moving, as though the dread were a physical pain I would provoke below my ribs. Sunlight moved in the room. Where did childhood go? Pain of memory... where all the places I loved, where all the people...other people don't get scared like this... it will go away, I know, but it's terrible now... All this before I lifted my head and saw John, head thrown back against the couch, one hand still resting on my ankle in his lap.

"John," I said, and my tongue felt like wool. "You've got to catch a plane."

It was only 7am. We stumbled about, collecting his luggage, then I walked with him to the station. We were both subdued, nursing our heads, wishing we were asleep between cool white sheets. The idea of a journey to Australia was remote as a tiny island in a far-off sea.

"Can't believe it," John said indistinctly as we stood, squinting down the line. It was his only concession to the size of the trip he was about to start. "Put a stone rolling and look what fuckin happens."

I walked to a bench and sat down gingerly.

"I feel terrible."

He shrugged the heavy rucksack off and dropped it beside me with a grunt. We sat in silence till we saw the train, far off, a silver ribbon moving painfully slowly up the track. The approach of the train threw us into an uneasy kind of dither. We stood, and John fiddled with the rucksack, adjusting straps and checking all the zips were closed. I walked down the platform a little way, wishing there was more time, that we had the whole morning to sit and talk it over in a café. I turned back to John, feeling an impulse to snatch more time.

"Will I come to Heathrow"

"To the airport? Why?"

"I want to. I want to talk to you a bit."

He shrugged. "Do, so. It's a hell of a way. You'll be late for work."

"Who cares?"

The train was closer now. Caught in the trap of the decision, I had alternate visions of being on the train with John, and of walking slowly back to the house: Heathrow, the bustle of luggage trolleys and flight calls; my uncle's kitchen, quiet except for the hum of the fridge; waving to John at the departure gate; a cup of coffee. When the doors opened, John put a hand on my shoulder. His face looked grey, strained, even though he smiled briefly.

"Don't come with me Cam. I'd rather say it here, and then I'm off."

"Ok." I smiled too, happily. "I don't mind. It's just — I wanted to talk more. You know, find out things."

"Do you still think you'll come?"

"Yes."

"I'll write to you, tell you how to apply and everything." With his other hand, he stroked my neck gently, twice. "I think it's the right thing."

I looked away, over the roofs of the houses, to the ugly flats beyond. Then back to John, watching me.

"I don't know what's right," I said. "But however far I've come, it hasn't been far enough."

He went then, hauling the rucksack in and leaning it against the carriage wall. He came back out onto the platform and kissed me quickly, on the cheek.

"I'll see you," he said. "Off you go now."

"Write to me and tell me how to get a visa," I said. All the way down the road, I didn't look back, even when I heard the train start up, and it passed me on my right. I just raised my hand once as it went by, in case he was looking.

Rosita Boland

Arriving

1.
At intervals, the unseen pilots
Called out the names of the countries
We were flying over.

I studied the map on the back cover
Of an in-flight magazine,
Appalled, and exhuberant
At this contraction of the world:
Travelling, in twenty-one hours,
As far as it is possible to go
Without starting to come back.

2.
The Korean taxi-driver
Had never heard of Ireland
And I felt thrillingly rootless.

He told me that Sydney
Was in the middle of her October storms
And the only thing I took on that drive
Was the rain,
Racketing down the brightly-painted iron verandas.

3.

I had just fled from a hurricane
And the worst October weather for a century
But it seemed the rain had followed me here:
Falling in Biblical quantities, all day, every day
For the next three days.

Disorientated,
I threw my canvas shoes
And wandered barefoot through the rivery streets,
Sharing a black silk umbrella
With a Japanese boy who spoke no English.

4.

The silence
After the rain
Was so sudden it woke me up.

Standing at the window,
I saw my first clear Australian sky.
There was something extraordinary about the new moon.

I was looking at a mirror-image
Of a moon I had known all my life.
The points of its crescent
Faced the opposite way:
Exactly as something does when you look at it
From the other side.

Joseph O'Connor

Four Green Fields

The morning after the bomb, Eddie Virago had a serious case of the shakes. He swept back his straggling greasy quiff, leaned forward over his desk and continued forging the expenses docket for his training course in junior bank management, at the Royal Free College of Financial Services, Catford. The sun roared in through the office window, making him sweat and pant through his pursed lips, and the hum of the banjaxed air-conditioning only seemed to make everything worse. He unscrewed the cap of the tippex bottle and began to apply the white fluid to the dotted line, slowly, lightly, with the concentration and delicacy of a restorer of medieval paintings.

Suddenly, the telephone rang, making him start and fumble with nervousness. He opened a drawer and flung in the tippex bottle, snatched up the receiver and ran his fingers through his hair.

"Virago," he said, attempting efficiency. "Accounts."

"Eddie," said his sister's voice. "It's me."

"Patricia," he said, relieved. "Jeez, what's shakin'? How's Paris?"

"Great, Eddie. And you?"

"In the groove," he said. "Too damn hot though. London's always too hot in the Summer. It's making me anal as fuck."

"Eddie," she sighed, "what does anal actually mean?"

He thought about this for a moment. He picked up a pencil and wrote the word on his blotting pad. ANAL. He drew a circle around it.

"Ah, nothing, really. It's Freudian. How the Hell are you anyway? *An bhfuil tu ag marchaoicht?*"

"Eddie, listen, I've a bit of news."

He picked up his coffee and tittered. "What's that? You and Phelim getting hitched, is it?"

"No fucking way," she scoffed, and then paused, her words echoing faintly on the line. "Now don't get excited, Eddie, but I had this accident."

"What accident?"

She paused again. "See, I had this accident the other night. I'm in the hospital over here actually."

He felt his heart pulse.

"I got run over on Saturday night," she said.

"Jesus, Patricia. You're kidding me."

"No," she said to him. "I'm in hospital and everything. I got run over."

"Fuck. Did you get his number? Did you call the pigs?"

"Well, that's the thing. It wasn't a car, Eddie."

"What?"

"It was a train."

"*What?*"

Her voice started to crack with tears. "Well, I was plastered you see. I'd been out with Phelim at the Sting concert and we had a row on the way home. The little wanker told me Orla O'Hagan gave him a blowjob at some party when he was home at Christmas, and we were pissed, and I fell over onto the train tracks. In *Les Halles*. And a train came along and..."

"Patricia. You're pulling my fucking wire."

"I'm not," she whimpered, "I lost a leg."

He spluttered a mouthful of coffee over his shirt. "*WHAT?*"

"I lost a leg, Eddie. They had to amputate it."

"Fuck off Patricia," he tittered, nervously. "You're kidding."

"It's true," she shrieked. "I've only one leg."

The line crackled and bleeped. He felt sweat soak through his forehead.

"Jesus," he said. "Jesus."

"I'm so scared, Eddie," she sobbed.

"Christ almighty, Patricia. Are you OK?"

"Well, I'm a bit upset, Eddie. I ..." Her voice trailed into tears again.

"Patricia, this is...I mean, fuck me slowly with a chainsaw."

"Yeah, I know. Listen, can you ring Dad and tell him?"

He whinnied with high-pitched laughter. "No way," he said.

"Way," she whimpered.

"Christ, Patricia. Just run this by me one more time, OK? You want me to ring Dad and tell him some Froggie quack had to amputate your fucking leg?"

A tornado of tears came rushing down the line. "But he'll kill me if I do it," she wept. "He'll make me come home. I couldn't face it. Go on, Eddie. Will you? Please?"

"Patricia, I..."

"Look, I have to go now, Eddie, the nurse is here with my pills."

"Patricia..."

The line went dead and began to burble. He slammed down the receiver, stood up shaking and went to the window, trying to concentrate. His sister had one leg. It was eleven o'clock on a Tuesday morning and he was on the twentieth storey of an office block in London and his sister had just telephoned from Paris to say she only had one leg. He said the words out loud. One leg. One fucking leg. It was going to be one of those days.

Down in the streets he watched the gangs of workmen clearing up the rubble from the bomb. Some of the office buildings had been completely closed off, boarded up, surrounded by long lengths of yellow and red tape. Policemen were sifting through the ruins, picking up bits of stone and mortar and dropping them into black plastic refuse sacks. There were reporters and cameramen everywhere.

My sister has one fucking leg, he thought. My sister has one shagging leg. I got up this morning and I had cornflakes for breakfast and I read the paper and my sister had one leg. And it happened last Saturday, for Christ's sake. So when I went out to the Limelight on Saturday night, my sister had one leg, and when me and Evelyn were in the bath screwing on Sunday morning my sister had one leg. And when...

He came back to his desk, lit a cigarette, picked up the telephone and tried his father's line in Dublin. His fingers were shaking. It was engaged. He tried again, dialling the numbers very slowly, hoping that this would make a difference. Still engaged. He felt his heart throb. He tried again.

"Jesus, come *on*, Frank," he urged. "It's me, Eddie. Come on."

Still engaged. He sat down, took a deep drag of his cigarette and put his head in his hands. He had a sudden desperate urge to throw up. His sister had one leg. What the fuck was he going to say to his father?

"I think you should probably sit down, Frank."

"Why, Eddie? There's nothing wrong is there?"

"Take the weight off your feet, Pops," he would say. "Both of them."

Well, on second thoughts, maybe he wouldn't put it quite like that.

The interior of the tube train smelt of feet and sweat and hot rubber. He was peering over the shoulder of the slim Japanese woman beside him, trying to read an article about Madonna's new lip job, when the train suddenly shuddered to a stop in the tunnel. The lights flickered and hummed and then there was silence, except for the rustling of several hundred copies of the *London Evening Standard*.

"My sister has one leg," he thought. "My sister is a fucking monopede."

The engine rumbled into life and cut out again. "It's a bloody disgrace," one old woman said, suddenly. "It's an absolute bloody disgrace, that's what."

"Oh yes," said another old woman. "It is."

He looked around the carriage at the tired red faces. A young couple by the carriage doors began to kiss. The boy put his arm around the girl's waist and pulled her to his chest. She raised her arms and put them around his neck. The boy moved his thigh between her (two) thighs and she gave a soft sob of laughing pleasure before pushing him gently away. A handsome Asian man in a white suit and a red turban began to whistle. With a dull throbbing sound, the train moved off again.

It pulled into Leicester Square station and the doors opened with a squealing sound. He climbed the escalator, feeling exhausted and hot, his head pounding with tension. In the vile-smelling tunnel, there were enormous posters for films and rock concerts, and someone had drawn cartoon genitals and breasts on the figures with a flourescent marker. A sad looking busker with a dog tied to his feet was playing a mandolin and hamming up the words of an old Irish song.

Ah sure, hung, drawn and quartered
Well that was me sentence
Condemned as a rebel, a traitor a spy
But no man will call me a knave or a coward
A hero I've lived and a hero I'll die.

Eddie felt the hot damp air on his face as he sprinted up the steps to the street and crossed over to the doors of the Hippodrome. She was not there. He looked at his reflection in the black glass of the windows. He thought about his sister and her one leg and for some reason he wanted to laugh now. It was terrible news, but he wanted to laugh, the way newsreaders do, when they have to read out something dreadful. His sister had one leg. It was funny, in some odd way. She had one leg, and it suddenly occurred to him that he didn't even know which leg she had. Jesus. Was it the right or the fucking left? He wondered if he could ring the hospital and ask. Which leg, please? He scratched his head and tried to remember. *Quelle jambe, monsieur le docteur, s'il vous plaît*? Was that it? Would that do? Leaving Cert French just did not cover situations like this.

The tarmacadam street surface sucked the sunshine into itself, and the doleful thud of heavy metal music pounded out from the packed interior of one of the tourist bars. He pressed his aching face against the glass. It felt oddly cool. He looked at his image again, smooth in the reflection. The knot in his tie was the size of an orange. He undid it and tied it again, and it looked a little better now. The armpits of his suit smelt musty and ripe, and when the buttons of the jacket were closed it felt a little too tight. He thought he heard her call out his name, but when he turned around there was still no sign of her.

Charing Cross Road seemed to shimmer with heat. Light poured from the pale blue sky and smells drifted out from the cafés, strong coffee, stewed vegetables, spiced beef and fried onions. A long line of Hare Krishnas shimmied around the corner of Leicester Square, banging drums and chanting. A tall languid girl in an open white shirt, black bra and flower-patterned flares ran across the street, carrying a portable television. Outside the tube station, the newspaper man called out softly to the passers-by. "*Standard, Evening Stan-dard*." A hoarding by his feet was daubed with black words. LATEST ON PROVO CITY BOMB.

Eddie closed his eyes and thought about this bomb. It had gone off last night, at the same time that his sister was lying in the hospital in Paris with one leg. He could almost hear the roar, almost see the shattering of a thousand windows, the shards of glass raining from the clouds, the skyscrapers slumping to their knees like drunkards in church doorways. He felt a little sick.

Suddenly he felt her arms twine around his waist from behind. "Hi," she said. He turned and kissed her on the cheek. She had on a bright red knee-length dress, a black silk jacket. He wanted to laugh out loud because she looked so lovely.

"Look at you," she said, "a terrible beauty is born."

"It's an old suit," he said.

"It's gorgeous," she said, "but did your Mammy never learn you to tie a tie, no?"

He loved her accent, its Northern inflections and rhythms, the music of its vowels. It always surprised him, filled him with a strange kind of wonder. He knew this was absolutely ridiculous, but it was true anyway. She reached towards him and kissed the corner of his mouth, sliding her tongue briefly between his lips.

"You look lovely," she said.

"Yeah, listen, Evelyn..."

She glanced at her watch. "Are you right?" she said. "We're really late, Eddie. My zip went. I'm putting on weight."

"You're not," he said.

"Maybe I'm pregnant," she grimaced. "Wouldn't that be great?"

"You're not pregnant."

"No," she said. "You drink too much. Your sperm wouldn't be strong enough. If I gave birth to anything it'd be a bottle of tequila."

She turned around and half slipped off her jacket. Her neck and her bare shoulders were lightly tanned. Suddenly he remembered the hotel room in Paris, the afternoon they had come home early from the Louvre and made love, the stale croissant crumbs in the bed, the chatter of tourists down below in the narrow and echoing street. Her hand moved around to the back of her neck and touched the top of her spine.

"Is it alright?" she said. "My zip?"

He nodded. "Listen, Evelyn, there's something.... "

She glanced away from him, stepped quickly into the street and waved her small handbag. The taxi pulled up, leaking diesel fumes. The yellow light on the top flickered out.

"Euston Road Registry Office," Eveleyn said. "You know it?"

The driver gave a sullen nod. They jumped in and sat down and the taxi began to pull away up Charing Cross Road.

Outside Waterstones, a young black woman with a child in her arms stepped suddenly off the pavement and into the road. The taxi swerved and rocked to a stop. The driver rolled down his window and stuck out his head.

"Blind fucking cow," he roared. "Look where you're fucking going, can't you darling, alright?"

The woman raised two fingers at him and turned into a side street. He sat very still for a moment, staring into the line of traffic ahead of him, cursing and muttering. Then he raised the hem of his greasy polo shirt to his face and dried his soaking skin with it.

"This fucking country," he sighed.

"Are you alright?" Evelyn asked.

"Fuck me pink," he muttered, shaking his head. "And we're supposed to fucking *like* them these days."

Moving slowly up Charing Cross Road, across Shaftesbury Avenue and onto Tottenham Court Road, the traffic was absolutely terrible. British Telecom workers had dug up a long section of the street outside the Dominion Theatre, and there was a fire brigade parked at the entrance to the tube station. Firemen were running around looking efficient as they unrolled hoses and handed out axes to each other. The inside of the cab was stiflingly hot. It smelt of leatherette and lemon air freshener.

"Evelyn, I..."

She turned to him, licked her finger and ran it along his eyebrows.

"Mammy rang this morning to say Uncle Peter might be over from home. You'll like him."

"Yeah, Evelyn, there's something..."

"Now Eddie, listen, try to be sociable today will you? And stay off the politics with Roisin. She's a bit of a chucky-head. But a bride is entitled to peace on her wedding day."

"What's that?"

She folded her arms. "A wedding day? Well, you see, it's when two people..."

"No, smartass. A chucky?"

She smiled. "Do they not have chuckies on the Southside, no?"

He shrugged. "I don't know."

"*Tiocfaidh ar lá*," she explained. "Chucky, you see. It sort of means a Provo."

He nodded. "OK. A chucky. Like you."

"Her aulfella was interned," she said, ignoring him. "He was put in the Curragh in the fifties, with all my uncles and my Dad."

"Your Dad was interned?"

She turned and gaped at him. "Sure, I often told you that before," she said. "Remember?"

"You never did, Evelyn."

"Course I did. I told you that night in the Mean Fiddler."

"You didn't," he pouted. "How come I'm always fucking wrong?"

She shook her head and her face liquefied to a smile. "God, Eddie. You're so gorgeous when you're in a snot."

She glanced at the driver through the glass partition, then leaned in close to Eddie and whispered.

"You know what? I'd love you to just pull my knickers down and lick me now."

"Evelyn, Jesus..."

"Must be the heat," she said. "But God, I'd love to be just feeling your tongue inside me now."

She grabbed his hand and moved it to her bare knees. He turned away from her and looked out the window. Evelyn had two legs and his sister had one. In the limb department, his sister was deficient by twenty five per cent. His sister was appendagely challenged in a very big-time way.

"What's up with you?" she said.

"Nothing."

He decided not to tell her. He would save it up for later. That would bloody well show her. Yes. That would teach her, if he said it later. Oh, by the way, Evelyn, I know you're having a really great time with your hayseed culchie relations here, but my sister was hit by a train and she had to have her leg off last Saturday, and I thought you might like to know. It might come in handy if she was enjoying herself too much. He didn't like Evelyn enjoying herself too much. It felt uncontrollable to him.

She began to hum a tune, tapping her fingers on her handbag. On Camden High Street, an ugly man in a tartan kilt and a studded leather T-shirt was selling watches from a large suitcase.

She poked his thigh. "Are you alright today, Eddie?" she said. "Is there something on your mind?"

He shook his head. "Biorhythms," he said. "They're bad for your heart."

"Oh, do you have one of those?"

"You're hilarious," he told her. "You crack me up."

"Don't be such a dry shite," she said. "If you don't want to come you can just go home."

He turned to her, doing his best to look hurt. "I do want to come," he said. "That doesn't mean I have to fucking like it."

The registrar was a beautiful Pakistani woman who couldn't seem to stop smiling. She had a gentle and calm voice, and she seemed to be enjoying herself. But the bride was trembling so much that the groom started to laugh at her half way through, and the registrar told them they could both sit down during the ceremony if that made things easier.

"By the power vested in me by the London Borough of Camden," the registrar nodded, "I now pronounce you man and wife."

She looked up. "And now," she said, "A round of applause for the bride and groom, I think."

Everyone clapped, except the bride's mother, who looked furious. The registrar peered down at her and shrugged.

Evelyn turned to Eddie and whispered in his ear. "Aunty Mamie is bulling because it's not a church job."

"Because the fucking groom is English, you mean."

She shook her head. "It wouldn't be that. Uncle Martin would be more upset about that."

People started queuing up to kiss the couple, the children jostling and pushing each other out of the way.

"Do you know all these heads?" Eddie hissed.

"There's a lot of relations from home. I didn't think so many would be over. I hope Uncle Peter comes."

A young and spectacularly handsome man in a sharp red suit grinned at Evelyn from across the room and began to chuckle and wink. The bride's mother glared at him, and he looked embarrassed.

"Who's that, Evelyn?" said Eddie.

"Just Wiggy," she whispered, blushing. "He's from Birmingham. He used to be in the squat with me and Fidelma when I came over first."

"He looks like an awful dickhead. What's he like?"

She shrugged. "I went with him a few times," she said, and she sniggered guiltily. "He knew what was what."

Outside on the steps, someone opened a bottle of sparkling wine and it spurted all over the groom's trousers. Down on the Euston Road a bald drunkard in a sailor suit started to roar and wave his fist at the passing lorries. *BASTARDS. BASTARDS, SONS OF BITCHES ONE AND ALL.* The registrar took a photograph of everybody. The bride said she didn't want anything to drink. She was definite about it. She said it wouldn't be good for the baby, and her mother turned and looked away, shaking her head.

Outside the Camden Irish Centre the cars were double parked. A group of young black men in baggy trousers and baseball caps kicked a soccer ball to each other. Loud raggamuffin music was blasting out of a portable tape machine on the footpath.

The John F Kennedy Function Room had been decorated with flowers and tinfoil stars and strings of green and orange bunting. White plastic tables and chairs were arranged around the edge of the wooden dancefloor. Women in aprons were moving between the tables, polishing glasses and folding red paper napkins into cone shapes.

Eddie sipped tensely at his third pint of Guinness and looked around at the guests. You could tell which ones were Irish, somehow, but he did not know exactly how. A waiter brought in a huge tray of drinks and put them down on a table. The groom's family were sitting by themselves in the corner, looking restrained and politely uncomfortable in their hired suits.

He found himself wondering about his parents' wedding day. He remembered his mother telling him about it once, before she had left his father. It had been a bright day in April, and the drink had run out early. They had gone to Barcelona on their honeymoon, and stayed in a little hotel in the Bario Gotic. That was unheard of in those days. Nobody from Crumlin went anywhere like Barcelona for a honeymoon. He thought of his mother's laughing face and panic suddenly flowered in his stomach. He realised that someone would have to tell her about Patricia, and he realised that it would probably be him. He had not seen her for nearly six months now, and it was not going to go down well, the story of Patricia and her missing leg.

Where was it? Where was the leg that had been cut off? Had a bit of it just been left lying there on the train tracks, and had some manky Parisian pervert taken it home as a souvenir? Or had someone thought to pick it up and put it in a bag and bring it to the hospital? Would they be able to make her a plastic one? Or a wooden one? Hadn't the guy who invented the Muppets developed some shit-hot technique for making artificial legs? A dreadful memory leapt up. He had once seen a man in Earls Court Tube Station pull up his trouser hem and unscrew his wooden leg. It had had a shoe and a sock on it, and he had just unscrewed it, fiddled around with it for a minute, then attached it to the stub of his knee again, sitting on the bench in the tube station. He shuddered at the thought.

He looked around the room, wishing he was somewhere else. He did not know where Evelyn was now, and he felt uneasy, and already a little drunk. People started to come in from the bar. Somebody put on a record and a few of the younger people started to dance around. Then two old women began to waltz together, even though the record was a rock and roll song, and not something you could easily waltz to. They waltzed as though they had learnt the steps out of a book. He watched the other couples jiving and found himself thinking about his sister once more. He remembered her dancing with Jimmy on the night of his twenty first birthday, dancing around for hours, and he realised that his sister would never be able to dance again. That struck him as appalling, for some reason.

Across the dancefloor, the young man in the sharp red suit was jitterbugging efficiently with a beautiful blonde woman in a tight black skirt and a tigerskin blouse. He held her hand, pushed her away, pulled her in close to him, raised his hand in the air and whirled around her. Suddenly she jumped in the air and wrapped her thighs around his waist, and everyone laughed and clapped, as she jumped back to the floor and shook her hips.

"Fucking prettyboy," Eddie mumbled.

Just as the record was ending, Evelyn tottered into the room looking drunk and lost. She beckoned to Eddie and he came over to her. Then she took his hand and tapped the young handsome man on the back. The blonde woman smiled and said she had to go to the bathroom. They watched her walk away, wiping her face on the sleeve of her blouse.

"Trying to get your hole already, Wiggy," Evelyn said. "God. Where did you pick that dancing up?"

He shrugged and pushed his hair out of his eyes. "Along the way."

"You're fabulous at it. You must teach me some time."

"I'll teach you later," he laughed, glancing at Eddie.

"Oh," she said. "This is Eddie Virago, This is Wiggy Thompson."

"Alright matey?" he said, shaking Eddie's hand. A sudden ray of bright sunshine burst into the room from the upper windows. Evelyn said she was going to the bar.

"You're Irish then?" Wiggy said, in his Jasper Carrott accent. Eddie nodded and sipped at his beer.

Wiggy gazed around the room as though he was looking for somebody. "Terrible what we're doing over there, man," he murmured. "I don't agree with it at all."

"Yeah."

"See, I'm in the Socialist Workers Party. We're very anti, you know what I mean? I mean, everything that's going on over there like."

"Oh are you?"

Wiggy threw his eyes to the ceiling. "Fucking Major. Imperialist fucking tosser."

"Yes."

"And James Connolly, man. Hell of a guy."

"Yeah, right. I suppose he was."

Wiggy closed his eyes and shook his head. "Hell of a guy," he said. "Just terrible what's fucking going down over there in Ireland."

The dinner was chicken and fizzy potato salad and slices of greasy wet ham. When Evelyn asked the waitress where the chicken came from, she said Tesco's in Neasden, and Eddie said it tasted like it had walked the whole way and then given itself up.

The speeches started. The best man said he was looking forward to getting a framed picture of the happy couple, "preferably mounted," and everyone laughed. The groom stood up and thanked everybody for their help. When he mentioned the name of the bride's mother she stared down at her plate and began to finger her fork.

As the after-dinner drinks were being served, Eddie noticed a very old thin man on one crutch come shuffling into the room, with a black patch over his right eye. A couple of the guests jumped up and ran to him as he began to limp painfully across the floor. He shook hands with some of them, kissed some of the women, then nudged one of them, pointed down at Evelyn and put his finger to his lips. Then he edged painfully over to the table and tapped Evelyn on the back. She turned.

"Uncle Peter," she cried, jumping up. "I wasn't sure you'd be over."

He hugged her hard, kissed her cheek and then slapped his chest, panting slightly. His voice was very frail.

"Oh well, Jackie Ryan ran me up to Belfast and I wandered over on the British Midland at twelve. I was treated in fine style." She threw her arms around the old man again and hugged him tightly, tears forming in her eyes.

"Eddie," she said. "This is my uncle, Peter Toner."

The old man's fragile voice was high-pitched with excitement. "I'm delighted now to meet you, Eddie. We've heard all about you over at home."

"You have?" Eddie said. "Really?"

"Eddie's a bit of an intellectual, Uncle Peter," Evelyn said. "He went to the University in Dublin. He's as clever as anything."

The old man inclined his head and smiled. "What's that, Pet?"

"He was in the *University* in Dublin."

"Oh yes. And what's this you were studying, Eddie?"

"English."

"Sorry?"

"English literature."

"Novels is it?" Peter Toner said, so quietly that they had to move closer to him.

"Well yes," said Eddie, "and poetry."

The old man sighed. "I used to enjoy poetry." Then he looked up at the ceiling and closed his one good eye. "The splendour falls on castle walls, and snowy summits old in story. The long light shakes across the lakes..." He peered at Eddie and licked his lips. "Who's this wrote that one?"

"I don't know," Eddie said.

Evelyn tutted and put her hands on his hips. "He's no use to anyone, Peter. Sure, he's an awful eejit."

"Pardon me?"

"He's a bit of an *eejit*, Love."

"Oh, indeed he's not, I'm sure. But isn't it funny, the way they call it *English*, Eddie, all the same, when all the best practitioners are Irish? Isn't that the right word, Eddie. Practitioners?"

129

"Yes. I suppose it is."

"Yes. Practitioners."

Evelyn took her Uncle by the arm, led him to a chair and poured him a glass of wine. In the far corner of the room, surrounded by her friends, the bride's mother seemed to be crying. A woman was on her knees beside her, holding her hand and offering her tissues.

"Uncle Peter," Evelyn whispered. "Do you think Auntie Maureen will get over Roisin's news?"

He tapped his ear. "What's that, *a stor*?"

"Roisin's *news*. About the baby coming so soon? Auntie Maureen was saying earlier it was an awful thing to be getting married in white when you're in that way."

He shrugged, slopping some of the wine over his shirt. "Oh well, weren't they engaged? And isn't it only the natural thing anyway. There's nothing wrong with a bit of affection."

"Well," Evelyn said, teasingly, mopping at his chest with a napkin, "isn't it against the Church though, Uncle Peter, before you're spliced?"

He clicked his tongue with exasperation. "Some of these crawthumpers. They never had a woman in their arms, and between you and me now, love, that's their trouble."

"God, you're terrible," Evelyn laughed. "But poor Darren was saying he's dreading the birth all the same."

"Who?"

"Darren, Pet."

"Karen?"

"No, Darren. Her husband. He was saying he wouldn't be going into the hospital with her."

"Is he sick?"

"No, love. When she's having the baby."

Her uncle coughed violently and turned away. "Oh but that's a big thing now. All the young husbands do go in."

She slid her arm through his and her voice took on a lightly sarcastic tone. "I'm sure now that you were there with Auntie May when Muiris and the twins were born?"

He shook his head. "I never had that privilege. Though I don't mind saying they were the happiest days I had in my life."

"They're great when they're that age," Evelyn laughed.

"Pardon me?"

"They're *great* when they're *young*, Peter."

"Oh, great fellows," he agreed, squinting, phlegm catching in his throat. "After a few years though, they're nothing but lip. One word from their old fellow and they go to the fair altogether."

He pulled a handkerchief from his pocket and wiped his mouth. "They do what they like," he said. "But there we are. It's all ahead of you, eh Eddie?"

"Is your wife here, Mr Toner?" Eddie asked.

"Speak up there, son. I'm a trifle deaf."

"Eddie's asking you about Aunty May, Peter."

The old man snuffled and turned his face away. "No, son. I lost her last year."

"Oh. I'm sorry."

He nodded. "She was a lovely girl, God rest her. I was a lucky fellow, that she ever took a shine to me. We were great pals. But it was a merciful release for her in the end."

He sipped his wine with a shaking hand, then raised his finger and pointed. "I often thought she was a bit like Evelyn there. She had the same laugh as your *grá gheall* there. Full of the same bloody mischief."

"She was a dote," Evelyn said. "We all miss her."

He reached out and took her hand, squeezing it.

"Well I still have the little word with her every day. Upstairs, you know. She keeps a good look out for me."

"You'll need somebody up there anyway," Evelyn said, blinking back tears, "to put in the speak for you."

He chuckled softly. "Isn't she an awful rip, Eddie? And you'll have your hands full now, with that one."

She leaned towards him and touched his arm. "Sure, he often does Uncle Peter," she said. "And he's only fantastic too."

"What's that, Pet?"

"He often does have his hands full of me."

"Jesus, Evelyn," Eddie sighed, glaring around the room.

"My God almighty," Peter Toner laughed. "I'll have to go to confession if I keep on listening to this one."

A short and stocky old man with a moustache and a pale face came over to the table, carrying two pints of Guinness.

"Is it that blaggard Toner?" the man shouted. "Would you look at the bloody get up of it. Is the suit paid for yet?"

"That's Sean Moylan anyhow," Peter Toner giggled, standing up painfully and turning. "I'd know that auld bowsie a mile off." The man put the pints down on the table and took him in his arms, and the two embraced, clapping each other on the back. "How's the man? It's great to see you, Peadar."

"Oh, sure, I'm still going anyway, Sean. You've met my niece, Evelyn Doyle, and her young man, Eddie?"

"I've not had that pleasure," he said, shaking hands with Evelyn and then Eddie. "She didn't get the looks from your side anyway."

"What's that?"

"She's a lovely looking girl, Peter."

"Oh yes. She's the real ally daly."

"True enough. And how's the struggle *a Pheadar*? Any crack to be had?"

"Oh mighty crack, Sean."

"But you're looking fit to beat the band anyway. You must be running after some woman today."

"What's that?"

"Are you looking for a woman, is it, with the cut of you?"

Peter Toner laughed feebly. "There'd be no point. I'm too old for that carry on."

"Oh I'd say you've a little spirit left in you still, what?"

"Pardon me?"

Sean Moylan took Peter Toner by the hand and turned to Eddie and Evelyn, grinning broadly.

"I could tell you a few stories about this buck here. From the old days."

The old man turned to him. "What's that, Sean? Speak up?"

"Oh now, *Sinn Fein amháin*, Peadar. The friends we love are by our side and the foeman trembling 'fore us."

Peter Toner nodded, scratching his ear absent-mindedly. "God, weren't they great days Sean? Lord be with them. I find they're all in my mind now, as I'm shuffling on. And they buried poor Dan Farrell there the other week."

Sean Moylan pursed his lips and nodded. "There weren't many did as much as Dan."

"Pardon me, Sean?"

"Nobody did as much as Dan, I'm saying."

Evelyn's uncle clicked his tongue. "And I seen on the paper the family said no to the tricolour," he sighed. "They wouldn't even let the prayers be said *as Gaeilge*."

Sean Moylan nodded again. "But sure, there'll be more great days yet," he said, brightly. "The Republicans won't always be down."

"Pardon me?"

"There's better days coming, I'm saying. Better to come than ever was."

Peter Toner smiled. "Oh well please God, yes. And how's the *bean an tí*?"

"Well, she's saying she'll be off like that with some fancyman when we get the divorce over beyond."

"The...?"

"The *divorce*, man. It's coming in over beyond, they say."

"Oh yes. That's the next thing right enough, Sean."

Sean Moylan laughed. "She'd love to have seen you again, Peadar, but she's not too well since the by-pass."

"Who?"

"Maureen. She was only saying recently..."

"Oh yes. How is Maureen? Is she well, Sean?"

"Well yes, Peter. She's not too bad."

"That's good, that's good." The old man suddenly looked around the room, as though he didn't know how he had come to be there.

"But time is the enemy," Sean Moylan said.

"What's that, citizen?"

"There's *none* of us getting *younger*, Peter. Isn't that true?"

"Oh yes, yes." He peered around the room again. "Now tell us this Sean, is Maureen here?"

Sean Moylan glanced at Evelyn and winked. "We'll sit down now Peter and we'll have an old jar, what?"

"Come and dance," she said, taking Eddie by the hand.

She led him across to the middle of the dancefloor, put her hands around his waist and leaned her forehead on his shoulder. The room was very hot now, and it seemed empty of air. She looked up into his eyes and pressed her body hard against him.

"He's a bit gaga today," she said. "I'm embarrassed."

"Don't be. He's fine."

She smiled. "You look lovely, Eddie."

"So do you."

They circled slowly in each other's arms while the disc jockey played a slow song by Chris de Burgh. "Last night was lovely," she murmured. "I love it the way I can still feel you inside me the next day."

"We should have used something," he said.

She looked up at him. "I'm mad about you, Eddie."

He tried to laugh. "Don't say that, Evelyn."

"I suppose you'll run for the hills now. But I can't help it. I'm at your mercy."

He said nothing. She clicked her tongue and wrapped her arms tighter around his waist.

"What's on your mind today, Eddie? Are you thick with me or something? Is it being here?"

"It's nothing."

"Sure, tell me."

He sighed deeply. "Well, my sister had an accident in Paris. She had to have her leg amputated."

She stepped back from him, a look of disbelief on her face. "What? Patricia? Jesus, Eddie, you're joking me."

"Yeah," he nodded. "It's a drag, isn't it?"

"Jesus, Eddie? But you're not serious are you?"

"No, I am."

She put her hands to her head as though she had heard a loud noise. "My God almighty. Did you not say you'd go over to her?"

He slid his hands into his pockets, feeling awkward. "I didn't think. She asked me to ring up my father and tell him."

She looked into his face. "Fuck, Eddie," she said. "The poor dote. God, Fuck."

"Yeah," he nodded, "fuck is right."

The disc jockey put on "Stairway to Heaven." Over at the table, Peter Toner and his friend, Sean Moylan, were sitting down, watching them.

In the lobby, his father's phone was still engaged. So he went into the bar and had a drink by himself. Children were playing on the carpet, throwing crisps and peanuts at each other. He noticed Wiggy sitting with the blonde woman in the furthest corner. He had a pack of playing cards in his hand and seemed to be showing her some kind of trick. Three teenage girls were up at the bar, laughing together. Their accents were the same as Evelyn's and they looked like her too, with the same dark eyes and the same full mouths. A heavy-set young man wandered in and sat down beside them.

"God, Niall, is it you?" one of the girls said, kissing him on the face, "Fuck ye, you fat fucker." The other girls laughed. One of them turned around and seemed to notice Eddie. She half-smiled, then turned back to her friends and whispered something.

He sipped at his drink and found himself thinking about the night he had met her at the Engine Alley gig in the Powerhouse. She'd been up at the front, dancing with a few other girls. She'd been wearing a black miniskirt and black tights and a Sultans of Ping T-shirt. He had noticed her and thought she looked a little frantic. It was just after he'd split up with Salome, and he'd gone out to get wrecked with Jimmy and Ruth. He certainly hadn't been looking to meet anybody. But he'd just got talking to her up at the bar, when the surge of queuing bodies pushed them together. She was from a small town in the countryside near Carrickfergus, and she worked behind the counter in the Shamrock travel agency in Archway. He told her he had come over to London to be in a band, but it hadn't worked out, beacuse the others were less talented than him, and so now he was working in the bank, training to be a manager. It turned out that she had once met a friend of his from Dublin, Dean Bean, who was dead now, but who she said was the best looking man she had ever seen. When the gig was over, they'd stood on the path talking for half an hour, and then she'd asked him back to her flat for a drink.

When they'd got back to her place, it was very late and cold. Her three flatmates were lying together on a double mattress in the living room, under a quilt with no cover, watching the American Gladiators on the portable television, smoking joints, eating pizza and drinking cheap red wine from a litre bottle.

They had gone into her room, and she'd closed the windows and put on a tape of The Waterboys. She loved The Waterboys, she said, she had seen them play live a good few times now. They were going to be playing at the Fleadh Mór in Finsbury Park in the Summer and one of the fellows in work was going to get her a free ticket from a chap he knew who worked on *The Irish Post*.

They talked about music and films and drank a half bottle of musty *sake* which one of the girls had won in a spina bifida raffle, and which Eddie said was dangerous, and the reason Shane McGowan had got himself thrown out of The Pogues.

As she got more drunk, she said she missed Ireland. She got so lonely sometimes, and she wished she could go back home. But any time she did go home, she always wanted to come back to London after a week. It was the smallness of Ireland that got to her now, she said, the way everyone was the one colour, and knew everyone else. She always felt happy when the plane touched down at Heathrow, she said, and he told her that he knew what she meant. He told her if he ever got famous and had to fill in one of those stupid questionnaires in the Sunday papers about where his favourite place on earth was, he'd say the arrivals terminal at Heathrow Airport. Then she laughed, and he liked the sound of her laugh, and he told her that, and she laughed again more softly now, her eyes glittering in the murky light.

"You're gas," she said. "I'd say you could be trouble."

She asked if he wanted a joint, and he said no, he was trying to give it up. She said she never smoked it herself, although she'd taken ecstasy once, at an all night rave in Brighton, and it had made her feel horny. She loved to dance, she said. She never felt better than when she was dancing. At half past three, he looked at his watch and asked her if she had a minicab number.

She shook her head and looked around the room, avoiding his eyes. "If you wanted to stay, that'd be alright," she said.

She had taken off her skirt and tights and shoes and lain down on the bed in her T-shirt and underwear. He had stripped down to his Nelson Mandela boxer shorts, and she had laughed at them. They had got under the quilt and kissed and touched for a while, then fallen into a drunken sleep. And next morning they had woken up with terrible hangovers, and made love, while the sound of the dumper trucks and pneumatic drills down in the street had filled the room, along with the smell of frying grease. They had been going out for nearly six months now. They had even gone over to visit Patricia and Phelim in Paris. They were practically living together, but he still hadn't told any of his friends about her.

He went back out to the telephones and tried his father's number again. Still engaged. He rang the operator and she said the line seemed to be out of order.

He replaced the receiver and went back through the lobby towards the bar. An old man was sitting at the desk reading a copy of *An Phoblacht* and listening to something on a walkman stereo, his head bobbing in time to the music. As he crossed the floor, he saw her through the doors of the ballroom, slow dancing with an older man whom he did not recognise. He watched the way she laughed and ran her fingers through her hair. The man moved his hands to her waist, threw back his head and began to sing.

He came back into the bar, sat down at the counter and ordered another double whisky. Wiggy was still sitting in the corner, and he was kissing the blonde woman now. She reached her arm around his neck and pulled him closer to her. He put his hand on her knee.

"Irish or Scotch, sir?" the barman asked.

"Surprise me," Eddie said.

When he came back into the ballroom, she was sitting in a corner with Peter Toner and Sean Moylan. All three of them seemed to be drunk, and she was laughing very loudly, holding her hand up to her mouth. When he sat down beside her, he felt that the conversation had just been stopped because of his presence.

The plastic chairs had been arranged in a wide untidy circle around the tables, which had been cleared of dishes and plates. A few of the young men had guitars and fiddles and one had a bodhrán. People were arguing about who was going to start the singing.

"Any luck?" Evelyn said, peering up at him.

Eddie shook his head and said his father's line was still engaged. He sat down and took a sip of her drink. Wiggy came in from the bar, holding hands with the blonde woman. They came over and sat down beside Eddie and Evelyn, but Wiggy didn't seem to want to introduce his friend.

"Get up now, Martin," called Sean Moylan. "Give us a bar."

"Indeed I will not," the bride's father said, shaking his head. "I've no voice on me these days."

"Go on out of that," Peter Toner shouted. "Would you give us Sean South or something and stop your play-acting."

"Oh, there's a sly cove down there called Toner," the bride's father said. "He's a voice like a lark, but he won't sing himself unless he's three sheets in the wind."

The old man chuckled and blushed. "What's he saying, Evelyn?"

"He says you're a bowsie for not singing, love."

"On now, comrade," Peter Toner called out, and the people laughed again, and some of them clapped and cheered. The bride's father scratched his head.

"The Men Behind the Wire," a woman called.

"The Foggy Dew, Uncle Martin," shouted Evelyn.

He pursed his lips and scowled. "Ah, that's too much of a range for me these days. I'm not Pavarotti." Everyone groaned.

"Alright, alright," he laughed, "I'll give you another thing."

He stood up and bowed his head. "Well, God help us all," he said, and the people jeered him again. "What's this is the way it goes?" And then he lifted his eyes and cleared his throat.

The murmur suddenly stopped and silence came down over the room. He closed his eyes then, and started to sing very slowly, in a faltering baritone voice.

What did I have
Cried the proud old woman
What did I have
This proud old woman did say...

"Up, Martin," Evelyn shouted. "Shush," Peter Toner hissed.

...I had four green fields
And each of them a jewel

Till strangers came
And tried to take them from me

One of the young men started to strum his guitar, trying to guage the key. Some of the others turned to him, scowled and shook their heads, and the young man put his guitar flat on his knees, lit a cigarette and began to listen.

But my fine strong sons
Ah, they fought to save my jewels
They fought and they died
And that was my grief, said she.

"Lovely, lovely," whispered some of the guests, as he reached the end of the verse. Evelyn put her fingers in her mouth and whistled. The blonde woman laughed and sipped her drink. Over in the corner, the groom's family started to look even more uncomfortable.

"Jesus H Christ," Eddie sighed, putting his head in his hands.

...Long time ago
Sighed the proud old woman
Long time ago
This proud old woman did say...

Suddenly the bride's father's voice seemed to take on more power. He leaned forward and splayed his fingers out on the table, leaning his weight on it, sucking in a deep breath:

...There was war and death
Plundering and pillage
My children died
By mountain, valley and stream
And their wailing cries
They shook the very heavens
And my four green fields...

He paused and raised his hands, palms upward, in the air, and some of the people joined in the song with him, singing loudly, their voices soaring and filling the room.

...Ran red with their blood, said she.

The bride's father stopped then and laughed nervously. He seemed to have forgotten the words. He looked down at his wife and she whispered to him, but he did not seem to hear what she was saying. He began to sing the next verse, then stopped again, blushing, rubbing his lips with the back of his wrist. His wife stood up slowly and took him by the hand, and she looked into his eyes as she started to sing, smiling at her husband, leading him in the song. He nodded as they started to sing together. Her voice was very high and it quivered on the grace notes.

Long long ago
Says the proud old woman
Long time ago
The proud old woman does say
I had four green fields...

The bride's father shook his head bitterly;

...And one is still in bondage,
In strangers' hands
They tried to take it from me...

He clenched his fist in the air, and his voice seemed to crack with emotion as he sang.

....But my sons had sons
As brave as were their fathers.

He paused again, letting the words hang in the air. Then he and his wife sang the last few lines, stretching out the phrases.

....And my four green fields
Will bloom once again, says she.

He turned and threw his arms around his wife, kissing her hair, burying his face in her neck. She put her hands on his head, and then the bride jumped up and ran to her parents, hugging them both. Her father's cheeks were bright red now, and tears were streaming down his face as he sat back down. A loud roar of applause filled the room.

"*Tiocfaidh ar lá*," the bride's father shouted.

"Yeahh," Wiggy yelled. "Right *on*."

"*Maith fear*, Martin," called Sean Moylan. "You never lost it."

Eddie felt Evelyn's eyes on him. "It's a great song," she said. "Isn't it? It's awfully sad."

He felt the drink pulse through his veins, and the muscles tighten in his throat. "It's a load of fucking shite," he said. "Four green fields, my hole."

Her face purpled and she tried to smile. "Don't say that, Eddie," she said, quietly. "People have strong feelings, you know."

He took another mouthful of whisky and scoffed. "If they've such strong feelings what are they all doing living over here? If it's so awful why don't they fuck off back to the bog they came from?" In the corner of his eye he saw that Sean Moylan was staring at him now.

"It's only a song, Eddie," Evelyn said. "Sure, what harm is there in a song?"

"It's bollocks," he said.

She looked at him, lips trembling, then turned to her uncle. "Do you hear this awful West Brit, Peter?"

The old man turned, his one eye bleary. "What's he saying, love?"

"Leave it, Evelyn," Eddie sighed.

"He says it's all shite, Uncle Peter, about the four green fields. That's what they all think down in UCD. They're all too busy being cool to give a damn about anything else."

Peter Toner said nothing.

"I don't care about all that shite," Eddie said, bitterly, his voice taking on a high-pitched sneer. "Wrap the fucking flag around me. What a load of shite."

"He says it's all shite, Uncle Peter. Do you hear him?"

"Well," Peter Toner nodded. "Maybe he's right."

"He is *not* right," Evelyn snapped. "These fucking southside liberals. They want to hand the whole lot back to the Brits."

"They don't want that," Eddie said. "They want peace."

Peter Toner smiled. He raised his finger and wagged it from side to side. "Ireland and England should never be in bed together, son. There's no peace down that road."

"Well they are," Eddie snapped. "They *are* in bed together."

"Pardon me?"

"And what good's ever come from it, Eddie?" Sean Moylan said, angrily. "Will you riddle me that?"

"Ah would you go back to sleep," Eddie snapped, and the blonde woman sniggered.

Evelyn stood up, trembling with rage. "Don't you dare say that to him," she said. "How *dare* you. You little Glenageary fucker."

Sean Moylan laughed as he reached out and took her by the wrist. She sat back down, folded her arms and looked away.

"Eddie," said Sean Moylan, pinching the bridge of his nose, "I knew a fellow like you when I was in the Joy one time. Oh he was a little fellow from Tyrone, tiny now, but brave as you like. Bright as a sixpence, he was, always one for a good row."

"Beam me up, Scottie," Eddie sighed. "We're off."

He didn't seem to hear him. "Donnelly, his name was. Did you ever hear about him in the university?"

Eddie shook his head.

"I believe he wrote poems. I never saw any of them myself. But God now, poor Charlie had a heart like a tiger."

He turned to Peter Toner. "Do you remember poor little Charlie Donnelly, *a Pheadar*? God, he gave his all in the end."

"Who?"

"Charlie Donnelly?"

The old man looked up, his lips wet with thick saliva. "God, is Charlie here, Sean? Where is he?"

"No, Peadar," Sean Moylan sighed, reaching out and touching his hand. "He's not here. Sure you know he's not."

"Who, Sean?"

"Charlie Donnelly."

"Oh yes, poor Charlie D. He was shot out in Spain, was it?"

"Yes, it was."

Sean Moylan pulled a tissue from his pocket and began to dry Peter Toner's mouth, as his one eye moistened with tears.

"Don't upset yourself now, *a Pheadar*."

The old man shook his head slowly. "God, I'd love to see poor Charlie again, Sean." He took the tissue in his gnarled fingers and screwed it into a ball.

"He was such a lovely fellow, wasn't he Sean?"

"Well, you know, I'm saying he gave his all for the auld cause, Peadar, I'm saying he..."

"For what cause?" Eddie scoffed. "What did he give his all for? So we all end up having to come over here to England for fucking work? That's some independence, man. That's fucking beautiful."

"*Ciunas* over there," somebody hissed.

A young woman stood up and started to play a slow mournful air on a flute.

"That's the four green fields, man," Eddie slurred. "There's green fields all over the fucking world now, man, not too many left in fucking Ireland."

The smile froze on Sean Moylan's face. "Hold on now," he said. "Nobody's saying mistakes weren't made."

"What about the bomb yesterday?" Eddie said. "I suppose blowing up chartered accountants for a United Ireland is a great idea?"

He looked into his drink. "That's not for me to say. That's for others to say."

"Convenient," Eddie said.

Sean Moylan nodded. "There was a lot of bravery in the old times, all the same. And later too." He turned and pointed at the bride's father, his voice trembling. "That man there was put away by the so-called Free State. A man who gave everything for his country. And gave it without a thought too."

"Fine Gael fuckers," Evelyn muttered. "Take it down from the mast, Irish traitors."

"Yeah. Damn right," Wiggy slurred. "Free State bastards."

Eddie turned to him. "Wiggy, man," he said. "Would you ever take your head out of your Birmingham arse and fuck off back to the Polytechnic?"

The blonde woman spluttered with embarrassed laughter. "That's lovely talk from an educated person," Sean Moylan said, folding his arms. "The young people today haven't a notion of what had to be done, sure they don't, Peadar?"

"What's that?"

"No," Eddie said. "No. They do actually, it's just they don't care any more."

Sean Moylan nodded. "This lovely educated fellow here says the young people don't care about their history, Peadar. Isn't that something now?"

Peter Toner looked up at Eddie and tried to smile, his head quivering, his one eye half closed. "Well sure, maybe that's what we fought for," he said. "So you'd have the right not to care, if ye didn't want to." He peered hard at Eddie, nodding, pursing his lips. "Did you never think of it that way?"

Eddie drained his drink. "No, I didn't," he said.

"You're only a fucking West Brit," Evelyn snapped. "West Brit."

He put down his glass, stood up and started to walk towards the door, bumping into the groom, who was hopelessly drunk now and staggering around in an embrace with his best man, crying and telling him how much he loved him. Half way across the empty dancefloor she caught up with him and grabbed his arm.

"If you walk out that door you can fuck away off. I don't ever want to see you again."

"Fine," he said. "I'm rattling."

She turned away from him suddenly sobbing, bowed her head and wiped her eyes. He reached out and touched her face, but she slapped his hand away. "You had to spoil everything," she wept. "You just had to. You're the driest little shite I ever met in my life."

"Oh thanks. Fucking thanks. What about my sister's leg? Like, I'm real sorry here, Honey, but I've got more on my mind than the four green lousy fields."

Tears dribbled down her cheeks. "Ah, if it wasn't that it'd be something else," she scoffed. "You always have to take the good out of everything."

He grabbed her shoulders. "What about my sister's fucking *leg*? What about that?"

"Go and ring your old man," she said, eyes black with mascara, "for you're just like him anyway."

Then she turned, wiped her face again, and walked away, and he watched her as she went back to the table and sat down.

"My Jesus, Eddie," his father said. "That's awful news."

"Yeah. Look Dad, do you think we should go over or something? Do Ryanair go to Paris?"

"Yes. Oh God, yes. She didn't say which one, did she?"

"Which what?"

"Which leg, Eddie?."

"No, Frank, she didn't. Does that actually matter?"

"God no. I suppose not. Feck it, that's awful news now."

"Yes," Eddie said. "I thought so."

There was silence for a moment and then his father started to snuffle with guilty laughter.

"Frank," Eddie said. "I don't exactly get the gag here. I mean sorry, I'm just having serious sense of humour failure here."

His father suddenly howled with mirth. "Patricia's as fit as you or me," he chuckled. "One leg, indeed. Sorry, Eddie son, I was in on the caper all along. Sure the two girls hatched it between them. They wanted to give you a bit of a land."

"What?"

He cackled again. "I thought you'd cop on in thirty seconds flat. Otherwise I'd never have gone along with it."

"What, Frank?"

"Your beloved and your lovely sister cooked it up between them, Eddie. Do you see? I thought you'd see it straight away. Did you not see the joke straight away, no?"

Eddie paused, his heart thundering. "Well, yeah, Frank. Course I did. Jeez, what do you think I am here?"

"Yes. It was only a leg-pull, son, oh ho, pardon the pun. But I knew you'd see through it straight up. One leg indeed. I told them straight. I said sure my son and heir would never fall for that, mark my words."

"I know," Eddie giggled. "Sheesh. What a gas, Frank, huh? I just fell around the place."

When he turned around she was standing in the lobby with a drink in her hand. He pointed at her.

"You're one fucking vile wagon anyway."

"I know," she grinned. "I'm sorry."

He stepped towards her, his face stinging with sweat. "Sorry? *Sorry*? No, the fucking Nazis were sorry, Honey. You're fucking... Jesus, this is so unbelievable."

"I didn't think you'd get so upset. I thought you'd cop on it was a wind-up."

He sat slowly down on the stairs and put his fingers to his cheeks. "I can't believe you did this, Evelyn," he said, shaking his head. "This is really something. I mean, gag me with a fucking spoon."

"Come back in for a bop," she said, taking his hand.

"You can just rev up and fuck off," he shrieked. "It's all over between us, Evelyn."

Her lip curled into a scowl. "Fine. Be like that, you whinging fucker. See if I give a damn."

"Fuck you too," he roared. "You poxy hag."

"And you're fat," she said. "That suit doesn't even fit you."

He held up his middle finger. "Swivel on it, Evelyn."

"I wouldn't waste my time, you lousy West Brit wanker."

By the time he got back inside, she had her shoes off, and she was dancing with the bride and groom, holding hands with them and jumping up and down in time to the music.

In the back of the minicab she held his hand as they sped through the empty streets of the city, both of them completely drunk now, and very tired.

Westminster Bridge had been closed off by the police barricades, and a long line of cars and lorries had built up. Plain clothes policemen were walking around the bridge with machine guns in their hands, and soldiers were searching the boots of the cars. The Big Ben clock said it was almost half past two.

The driver cursed under his breath, turned out of the lane and sped back down Whitehall, past Downing Street and the Ministry of Defence building, in the direction of Waterloo Bridge.

"Do you think we'll ever get married?" Evelyn said.

"Urgh, God," Eddie groaned, clutching his stomach. "I think I'm going to chuck up again."

The minicab driver flicked on his radio and wound it through the stations. A soft saxophone tune began to play.

"You had too much gargle," she said. "You'll be grand when we get home."

"Yeah," he swallowed, hot moisture filling his eyes. "Jesus, it was Barfsville Arizona earlier."

"We'll have a lie on in the morning."

"Patricia only has one leg," he giggled.

"She's legless," Evelyn laughed, and she kissed his neck. "Like yourself."

"You're one fucking wagon."

"I'm not," she said. "I'm sweet."

He rolled down the window and cool air flooded the car. "Uncle Peter's never going to speak to me again, Evelyn. He's going to put a contract out on me."

"He told me he thought you were great."

"Oh yeah. I'm sure he did." He looked out and up at the sky.

"He's dying, Eddie," she said, quietly. "He's riddled with cancer. He'll be gone in a few months."

The driver started to hum along with the music.

"He'll be gone by Christmas, they reckon."

"I'm sorry, Evelyn. Jesus."

She reached out and took his hand between hers. "There's something about a wedding, though."

"Mmmyeah," he sighed, leaning his head back. "I'm going to heave my fucking ring up any minute. I know it."

The car moved up Northumberland Avenue, around by Charing Cross Station, onto the Strand and towards Aldwych. The streets were quiet and dark as they drove back down in the direction of the river.

"So did Roisin enjoy her wedding day?"

"You know," Evelyn hiccupped, "she told me she went home this early morning to collect a few things. Only when she got there her Da had moved out of his own room and into hers. She went in, and he was asleep in there by himself, and it's only a little single bed, you know. And all his things were moved in, and her mother was still in the other room. Roisin said he looked like a little baby. He had his thumb in his mouth, you know the way babies do. And when he woke up and saw her standing there with her suitcase he started to cry, because he said he was going to miss her so much. And he told her how much he loved her."

"Really?"

She nodded. "It was the first time he ever told her that. Imagine."

As they turned into Lancaster Place and onto the approach road for the bridge, the blue flashing light of a police car appeared in the rear view mirror.

"I thought it was sad," she slurred. "To think of them in separate rooms, after all they went through. It was nearly like the end of one wedding and the start of another."

He leaned forward moaning and held his head in his hands. "Fuck, I'm gee-eyed."

She did not seem to be listening to him. She was staring ahead at the street, gnawing her lip. Then, after a moment, she turned to him and smiled and touched the side of his face. "God, I love you so much, Eddie," she said. "I really do love you so much."

He gazed at her, as the tears began to form in his eyes. "Yeah. Yeah, well, I love you too."

She nodded. "Try not to look so excited about it."

"Sorry. I get scared."

She put her hand on his thigh. "We'll be alright," she said, gently. "I wouldn't ever hurt you, Eddie."

The music played on, slow and sad. "I know," he shrugged. "It just makes me scared sometimes."

"But maybe we'll be lucky."

The car bounced over the security ramps. "Or chucky," he laughed, wiping his eyes.

"Lucky and chucky," she said. "That's OK. That's you and me."

The police car pulled out into the middle of the road and started to overtake. The officer in the driver's seat stared in at Eddie with a frown on his thin white face. He turned to the driver and seemed to say something, then turned back to look at Eddie again. He glared at him for a few moments and then the car accelerated and sped away across the bridge with its siren wailing.

"Lucky and chucky," she whispered, again, leaning her head against his shoulder. She took his hand, stroked it lightly and rested it on her breast. "Lucky and chucky."

Near the far bank, the police car stopped. The doors seemed to open very slowly. The two officers got out, stepped into the middle of the bridge and held up their white-gloved right hands.

The night was surprisingly cold. A fresh wind whipped up from the river. Gulls whirled around in the air, screaming and crying. Somewhere in the distance a burglar alarm was wailing. Thunder rumbled. Down towards the east, the dome of Saint Paul's towered over the city, and the blue lights of the NatWest Tower glimmered in the mist.

By the time they had finished searching the car, Evelyn was fast asleep in his arms on the edge of the pavement, breathing softly, and the sun was beginning to yellow the edges of the sky.

He held her tightly and kissed the corner of her mouth. She murmured and twined her fingers through his. And she looked so beautiful now, and so happy too, that for one long moment he did not even want to wake her up and take her home. But the taxi driver sighed and said he was in a hurry, and there was still a lot of work to do, and anyway, the morning was a little too cold for love.

Martin Meenan

Hard Love

I never come to places like this any more. I did once, knew them
well. That was before I got the Next suit and began doing very
nicely thank you among the liberal English classes. My accent
then had a kind of kudos. Then it became tiresome. Then I
dropped it. I'm glad I started drinking as soon as I got in. This
place makes me realise how far I've come. I was nicely on my own
but now the place is full and a fat woman and her friend are
crushed up against me. When I walked in I knew it was a mistake.
Community Centres have that smell about them, of poverty and
polemics and pressure groups and unaired rooms. The
noticeboard was layers deep in pinned paper, badly designed
adverts for African evenings or Gay support groups or
Assertiveness sessions. So what am I doing here, in a shitty little
hall on a Wednesday night at the end of winter. I look around at
the people. They are laughing too loudly. Determined to have a
good time. Desperate. The air is beginning to haze with smoke.
Everywhere else in London smoking is on the way out. Here
tonight its all lungs together, inhale. Perhaps the tobacco
companies are dumping their products on the Irish in England.
Like they do on the Third World. Don't these people read? Can
they read? What the fuck am I doing here. I'll stink tomorrow.
Staleness floating off my hair in a miasma of unwashed sheets.
Are these my people? Who are my people? Who gives a shit? The
Irish Club. The Irish Club in England. Now there's a thing. These
people didn't leave Ireland. They escaped. What the hell was left
behind? And how they love to be loved. Big open arms. Fat fingers.
Smug women. Double vodkas. Bitter for the Paddies. Guinness
for their sons. Irish men with London accents. An
embarrassment. Lots of drink and wait for the hooley to begin. A

secret language. The craic. Who spelt it like that? A reputation to keep up. Ordering shorts for people who are driving . Saying ach go on now, one'll do no harm. Children all around the place. A gypsy encampment indoors. A tinker's gathering of desperate people.

"Great night for the Irish. And where are you from?"

That's right, get your bearings, you fat old hag, with your soft southern voice and your stained fingers rattling.

"The North." That'll shut her up.

"Have you been over long?" Tell her now. Just give out a sheet, she'll get it out of you anyway. Is there much to get out? Not much.

"Since '78."

"Work?"

"University."

She's nodding there, all pleased. The Irish love education. Better than England. Even better than Scotland, and they're renowned. Feed her another morsel of your life.

"I've been working here since." Pause, she's looking at me. That's not a finished sentence in her book, "In publishing."

"Publishing? That's a good job now..."

How long has she been over here? Even the way you say it, over here. Your life has a relevance only in that it refers to somewhere else, back home. They spend their life in England, wanting to be somewhere else. She's going to ask about Northern Ireland. Come on, you stupid old bitch. One more drag of your cigarette. Stub it out in the soggy ashtray. A quick drink from the glass with lipstick on it. Your lipstick but someone else's as well. Two shades, two neon signs. You're turning to me, go on, say it.

"Good turn out, though, for the middle of the week."

She'll say it yet. I grunt and get up for another drink. Out of the shitty hall into the bar. Past the noticeboard with its signs for Disabled Access Support Group, Lesbian and Gay Advice Sessions, Drama for those from an ethnic minority. Why don't they just say it, cripples, queers and blacks. The Irish battering on about being the biggest ethnic minority in England. The letters in the *Irish Post*. Discrimination. Anti-Irish bias. Our children will be English. And if our children feel uncomfortable, their children won't. The truth is they're jealous of the blacks. A black's kids will still be black, and their kids, and their kids. It's only the accents that keep us Irish, and the history. That goes. It all goes. With maybe a rump of Irish dancing lessons. Or a name. Englishmen called Liam. English women called Siobheann. Too many vowels. Siobheann your knickers your mother's coming. Watching Gaybo on Channel 4 at five o'clock Monday. Happy as fuck when Ireland looks like going through to the World Cup. And the supporters are so good. Not like the English animals. A secret superiority. We know how to laugh at ourselves. Polite at the bar. Big rounds being bought in. Rough men with manners and one for yourself. A pint. The perfect product. The more you have the more you want the less able to count the cost. Back into the cavern, the smoke rising. Three men who work in Local Authority during the day playing on stage. Drums, accordion and guitar. First generation. They know all the tunes. Holding on. Holding on to it. Sit down again. She's turning to me.

"I saved your seat. On your own? We'll find a nice wee girl for you yet." She turns to the other witch she's come with and they both laugh. A faint rattle in their throats from the smoking. One begins to clap her hands. The other whoops as they look at the stage. On the floor a simpleton gyrating. People cheering him. He grins with stupidity. We look after our own.

"You're from the North, then. What's it like up there?"

There it is at last. The question. Where did she come from? Mayo maybe. Sligo. Three hours on an EC sponsored road would take her there. She's as likely to spend three hours on a plane to Beirut. What's the point in answering. I don't know any more anyway. On the stage a young man with greasy hair is getting up to read some poetry. He looks shy.

Probably some shite about the land. I turn to the woman. I haven't answered her question.

"Where's the toilets in here, hi?" I listen to myself putting on a Derry accent. Like taking a forgotten pair of flared loons from your wardrobe and playing air guitar in front of the mirror. She points. Expects me to be rude. I walk across the room. Up on the stage the lad is talking. He has a Northern Irish accent. Because of that I stop. I catch the end of what he's saying.

"...people from the South look at people from the North. It's called *Kalashnikovs for Heads*."

I stop to listen. There's me and him, perhaps a couple of others in this room. An ethnic minority in an ethnic minority. Pompous shit. I'm beginning to sound like the blurb on the dust jacket of some earnest first novel. He starts. He's nervous.

You think we have Kalashnikovs for heads,
And Armalites for limbs,
For hands, grenades.
You think that we park car bombs in our drives,
And every letter posted contains wires.
That we drink petrol to roughen up our tones,
And dunk thin slabs of Semtex in our tea.
You look at us and shake your head and ask
If we could just explain what's going on.
You just don't understand.
We shrug our shoulders muttering ach well,
There are bad boys on both sides,
But most are normal,
The friendliest you'd meet.
The countryside is beautiful, and yet,
And yet.
We look up to see what you might say,
But you still look confused,
But happy that we look as lost as you.
The answer brightens you.
When we are gone you call us Northern bastards.
And you are right.
You are afraid of us down South.
Afraid we'll take our language and our hate
And tarnish your reputation for being quaint.
You hate our hard edged accent, think we bleed
In orange or in green
After ripping at each other with our teeth.

You think of us as alien and strange.
And you are right.
You think we have Kalashnikovs for heads
And sit a distance in case we should go off
And blow your self deceptions all to hell.
The aliens have landed and are moored
Along your Northern border
And just wait,
Just as soon as there are barriers no more
We'll kick your soft green arses into shape"

There is a silence. I start to clap. I look over to where the two are sitting. They're looking at me clapping. Soft green arses. I love that.

Emma Donoghue

Going Back

Cyn kicked the machine systematically. She glanced down at Lou, who was scrabbling under the radiator for a pound coin. "Come on, wimp, help me kick," she told him. "I'm not letting you deflower me without a packet of Thick-Ribbed Ultras."

Lou's response was to embed his ears between his knees and gasp. Passersby were lingering at the nearby jobs noticeboard, all studious expressions and pencils in hand.

"So much for chivalry," Cyn announced loudly. "No rubber no jolly rogering. That's fifty pee I've wasted on you already."

She slung her scarred jacket over one shoulder and headed for the stairs. Lou hauled his red face up and stumbled after her. Once through the rainbow-muralled doors of the community centre into the noisy Brixton street, they let rip with laughter.

"Pathetic," Cyn reproached him. "Didn't they ever teach you how to keep a straight face in that seminary of yours?"

"If they'd taught me how to keep anything straight, sweetie, I wouldn't have been thrown out on my ear."

"Poor ear," murmured Cyn, flipping its pointed tip with one finger as they paused at the pelican crossing.

He writhed away. "That's sexual harassment of a co-worker, that is. And you who always meant to be a separatist."

"I'm a respectable woman now; I've been seen trying to buy condoms on a public corridor."

"Yeah, but which of us would have got to wear them?"

Cyn gave him a mistressful scowl. Then the skin around her eyes crinkled. "Did you spot May from Accounts at the noticeboard, ears flapping? Our reputations are saved."

They had met at Pride the previous June. Cyn, on a day off from her temping job, leaned her elbows on a steel barrier and watched the crowd whoop by. Lou was one of the boys in gleaming white jockey shorts, funking along behind the Sisters of Perpetual Indulgence. What made her notice him was the shamrock in relief on the back of his No. 2 shave; when he dropped out for a rest against the barrier, it was two inches from her face. The most testicular of symbols, she commented afterwards. Lou claimed it represented a triad of Celtic goddesses, but, when pressed, could not remember their names.

Then a few weeks later, on her way back from a James Dean double-bill at the Roxy in Brixton, Cyn happened to spot the Rainbow Centre and remembered something that nice boy-germ had said about working there as a set painter. Lou recognised the woman in the navy suit only when she hoisted herself onto the stage and introduced herself as "Whatshername from the march". She hadn't been on the boards, she said, since her days of teaching heel-toe in the parish hall under the knobbly crucifix.

August was nearly over when the two of them came face to sweaty face in Oscars. She reached over a line of men and bought them two lime and sodas. In return Lou remembered to tell her that they needed a dance person at the Rainbow to add a chorus of local ten-year-olds to *Fee Foe Fie Fum*.

It was one of Cyn's unspoken superstitions that if you met someone accidentally three times in as many months, the friendship had to happen.

She turned up on Monday morning, surprising them both. Over polystyrene cups of tea, her voice relaxed and dipped. Lou's ears recognised it as Irish, and he was suddenly awkward. He wiped his hands on a crusty blue rag. "You didn't tell me you were one of us."

"Who's us?" she asked.

"Ah, you know, Gay-lickers. Little green fairies."

"I've never felt like one of an us."

Lou let it drop. He led Cyn round the back of the set and pointed out details on a painted dragon to make her laugh.

As the first knot of kids trickled in, she stepped carefully over some chickenwire, introduced herself to them, and began inventing a Digestion Dance for Act II. Smacking her hip for the rhythm, Cyn stopped herself after one "*haon dó trí*", realising that these kids would have no idea what it meant. Somehow "one two three" sounded much flatter.

Two months slid by, three and a half, and Cyn was still working at the Rainbow. Or, as they variously called it on idle mornings round the drinks machine, the Rambo, the Brainrow, or the Puddle.

Lou she addressed as her toy-boy, her babe, her gentleman friend, her Martin Luther Queen. He borrowed her big leather jacket; she stole the last mouthful of his tea. The other workers didn't know what to make of them. Cyn and Lou didn't know what to make of themselves, nor did they worry about it.

One Friday in December Lou noticed her mouth sagging at the corners, so he dragged her to Oscars. "Would you go halves on a packet of crisps?"

She straddled a stool. "No point, English crisps are horrible. I stay faithful to Tayto Cheese 'n Onion."

"So you binge on them when you go back?"

Cyn spun a beermat on a fingertip. "Haven't been back."

"In how long?"

"At all."

Lou curled his feet round the bar of the stool. He tried to take it in. "What, since whenever?"

"1980. John Paul II was blessing ze young peepul of Iyerland as my plane took off. I could see the crowd shrinking behind the wing."

Lou bit the corner off his peanut packet. "Not even for Christmas?" He heard his voice, like a disappointed child's.

Cyn grinned over her upturned collar. "I suppose you'll be zooming home to the Mammy on the 23rd of December?"

"And stay till after the New Year's hangover. This year she wants me till Epiphany but I've told her we've a show on."

"Liar."

Lou bent his head. "Let's get the full confession over: I forget all my vegetarian principles when I smell the turkey stuffing."

And do you delight the family with your *Queer as Fuck* t-shirt?"

"Ah, get away with you." Lou's voice sank.

"Let me guess: you're not exactly out to them."

"Not in so many words, and certainly not in those particular words." Lou pulled at his ear lobe. You've forgotten what it's like back there."

"I remember too well." Cyn took a deliberate sip. "So why fold yourself back into the closet once a year?"

He made a face. "Because being a bit discreet is better than the ructions it would cause if I said anything. Besides, I couldn't miss the Christmas."

"Missing it's easy after the first time," Cyn assured him. "I get an old friend to send me a box of Tayto every year."

'But you must feel a bit... cut off."

"Ah get lost laddy." She looked at him with amusement that had a warning behind it. "Can you see me ever fitting in?"

Lou frayed the edge of his beer mat with one nail. "You wouldn't have to..."

"Listen, I felt more of an exile for twenty years in Ireland than I ever have in the twelve I've been out of it."

He contemplated the mark his glass had made on the polished wood.

Three hours later their speech was slower, more circuitous. The conversation had meandered through SM, the best temperature to drink Guinness, god, nephews and nieces, and was circling back to Ireland and its many embarrassments.

Lou knew some activists over there working for decriminalis-ation. Cyn tried three times to pronounce the word, and sniggered into her beer. She shut one eye and fixed him with the other. "What's the Irish age of consent, then?" she asked.

His forehead hurt. "There isn't one. I was telling you, it's a Victorian statute — "

"No," she interrupted him, "I mean what's the age of consent for being Irish?"

Lou was massaging his temples, too hard.

"I mean, I don't seem to remember ever being consulted. Correct me if I'm wrong." She pointed a stubby finger. "Were you ever asked if you agreed to be Irish?"

He shook his head carefully, once.

"All that cultural baggage foisted" — Cyn paused, checking the word — "absolutely *foisted* upon us without a by your leave." She continued, her finger dipping on every important word like a conductor's baton. "And what happens if you try and refuse it or leave it behind? Everybody freaks out as if you've dumped a baby in a carrier bag at the airport."

Lou opened his mouth, but could think of no remark that was not sad or silly.

Suddenly very much the personal secretary, she smoothened out a bus ticket and began a list of Reasons for Not Living in Our Dear Native Isle. It began to expand beyond the limits of the ticket, into rural depopulation and the violent habits of Celtic heroes, so Lou proposed they turn it over and restrict the list to new factors since 1980. On the plus side — Lou insisted there be a plus side, so Cyn drew a narrow margin down the edge of the ticket — all they could think of was crisps.

By the time he came back from the loo, Cyn had sagged over the counter. He could see a tear shining on the wood, and her shoulders were heaving. Putting one arm around her, he tried to shield her from the blank stares of the other drinkers.

After a minute, Cyn sat up and wiped her face on her denim sleeve. "Sorry."

"No problem," he said, too heartily.

"Christ," she roared, pointing one accusatory finger behind the bar.

"What is it now?"

"Page Three calendar. Typical bloody men. Even bloody faggots like a few bloody tits on the wall."

Lou got her out the door before the barman could take action. They walked in silence to the tube.

She cleared her throat with a husky roar. "Sorry. One pint too many."

"Sure."

"It wasn't about anything."

"Mmm."

Cyn turned a wet repentant face. "And what I said about faggots — I didn't mean you. I mean men are shits but you're alright, Lou — Lou."

"I quite agree." He pushed her through the turnstile. As she drifted towards the escalator he shouted, "You will receive my severed balls by the next post in a plain brown wrapper." He made a few jaws drop, but Cyn glanced over her shoulder and seemed comforted.

By the time they met up after Christmas, Cyn had worked her way through her box of Tayto. The next two shows were planned around gospel choirs rather than dance choruses; Cyn gave herself a week of moody unemployment, loitering in galleries and parks, then rooted out an old pair of navy tights and went back to temping.

One evening her Looptheloop came round to her flat for tuna bake. (Not that he was not a vegetarian, but somehow he always thought of tuna as a vegetable, just like anchovies.) He accepted seconds and thirds, to keep her company. Then they sat in front of the television with the sound turned down, and burped, and laughed in disgust at themselves. Each told the other they looked tired.

"Luther?"

He glanced up, startled by the full name.

She passed him the biscuit barrel. "Why don't you go out and have a wild passionate affair?"

"No particular reason."

"You're so post-Aids." Cyn sighed. "Have you calmed down after a riotous youth, is that it?"

"Not really. All through adolescence I painted trees. Then the seminary, painting Jesuses." Lou paused to remember, staring at the television screen, where a man and a woman were silently shouting at each other over a car door.

"And then a few wild oats?"

"No, then I hung around Limerick for a few years, wondering whether I'd go back to the seminary if they asked me. But in the back of my mind I knew well that the priests would never have me back without me volunteering for ECT or something. So finally I rolled up my vocation, left it under the bed, and took the boat over to London."

"And then some wild oats?" Cyn dipped another gingernut in her tea.

"One or two."

She rolled her eyes. "How can I be a faghag if my only fag is so damn respectable? I'm going to enroll you in a nude painting class tomorrow. You're in a rut."

"Am not."

"Are so. I can hear it in your voice."

"You're just projecting your rut onto me."

"Sounds painful!" she murmured.

Cyn didn't want to talk about herself tonight. She wanted to make fun of models in shampoo ads and maybe play Off the Couch if there was nothing on after *The Golden Girls*. With Lou she could almost touch the sixteen-year-old girl she'd never been.

Lou was sticking out his tongue at her lasciviously. "Don't you go inventing ruts for me. Those who can't live, counsel."

Cyn stared into the biscuity dregs of her tea.

It was a cold, clammy evening in March. Lou sat on the tube, counting the stops, reminding himself not to bend his ticket in case the machine would spit it back at him. He had four layers on to keep out the howling draughts; his face felt damp and hot. Cyn had rung to say he had to come over.

"What, now? Cyn-ful, I'd have to take three tubes."

"Please, I'm really sorry but please."

"Ok pet, no worries. Give me an hour."

Lou watched the grey wall of the tunnel hurtle by. Paper corners of old ads flapped in the breeze as the train came alongside a platform. Things had been strange with Cyn recently. Once they went dancing together in a dyke club which let boys in as friends or slaves on Mondays. He and Cyn had worn matching Pervert t-shirts, and danced like lunatics under a full moon, and in the toilet queue Cyn had told a curious woman that yes, Lou was her son, and she was very proud of him. It was a hilarious night, something to write home about, if his letters to his mother had ever told her anything that mattered.

But ever since, Cyn and he had been getting on each other's nerves. Silences and mishearing and prickliness; it seemed a silly way for a friendship to peter out.

On a lunch break last week, he had consulted Jazz, the counsellor at the Rainbow. Jazz advised sitting down together to share feelings and negotiate new terms. Lou nodded and squirmed. The best thing about friendship was not having to have all those heavy analytical conversations lovers had. Friends could just get on with living it.

His stop; he lunged for the door.

Cyn met him at the top of her stairs but didn't hug him. He had never known her to gabble quite like this. She told him how worried she was about the rumour that her landlord was planning to gentrify the block. Also she was thinking of changing to an agency which didn't mess temps around quite as much. The punnet of imported raspberries was a shocking price, but she had felt an urge to anticipate summer. Which laces did he think would go with her new boots?

Lou stayed patient until the third cup of tea. "Is anything the matter?"

"No, just wanted to see your ugly mug really."

"Any time."

Cyn sat on the arm of the sofa, her arms folded round a big patchwork cushion. Her feet tucked under the leg of his jeans, for anchorage. They watched a gorgeous dancer in a pop video.

"What a sulky face on your woman."

"It's a man in make-up," he told her.

"No way."

They argued the matter idly. She talked as if she had been drinking but her breath smelt of nothing but raspberries. Her fingertips were stained with them.

Lou accepted one, delicate-haired and slightly bruised. He kept his eyes on the television, nodding and keeping the occasional yawn inside his jaw. Only when he realised she was talking about the two of them did he look up and grin at her.

Cyn was telling him stuff he already knew but it was nice to hear it. How interesting it had been this year, something she had never done before, getting to know someone who was gay but of the opposite sex, like having so much in common yet being so far apart. It was the perfect situation for friendship, actually, because she was a completely woman-identified woman and he was, well, she supposed the equivalent phrase was a totally man-identified man, though that sounded a bit fascist, but she meant it in a nice way.

Lou assured her that he took it in a nice way. He stole the third last raspberry from the punnet in her lap.

Cyn was in full flow. How brilliant it was that the two of them could sort of share their thoughts without having them sort of curdled by heteropatriarchal patterns. (And to give her credit, she did grin as she dredged this phrase up from her feminist race memory.) A faggot and a dyke could balance each other, Cyn was explaining to him. They fitted. They knew who they were.

Lou nodded. His eyes slid back to the screen where Wogan was interviewing someone interesting for a change.

And then Cyn forgot what she was saying, forgot herself, and kissed him on the ear.

The rest was a blur to him, afterwards. He could never remember many details of that night. Maybe because he was so curious, so busy watching from outside, that he had not been really involved at all. Or maybe it was as if nature had edited out of his memory an experience irreconcilable with the rest of his life, like some women forget the pain of childbirth. But what Lou would always remember was that slow kiss on the ear that made every hair on his body stand up.

When he woke they were lying back to back. It was oddly comforting, the weight of his hip against the small of her back, her soles against his heels. The bed was damp, the wrinkled sheets still warm; he must have only dropped asleep for a few minutes.

Lou lay awake, not moving a muscle in case the two of them would become aware of each other and have to talk. He wanted to hold still and run it back through his head, but already it was blurring. The strange female shapes, the unexpected timing. And then, after all, the human similarity; the results of hands on bodies turned out to be not so different after all.

He had never been to bed with a woman before. Did it count if she was a lesbian? In some ways, Lou thought, stifling a giggle, it was the most logical choice.

Behind him Cyn shifted, her back pulling awake from his; a draught wound in to separate them. He had to move his leg or it would cramp. He twisted to face her, and rested his head on her shoulder, but lightly.

She found she could hear him thinking, like a pulse in the head on her shoulder.

"Hi," he said at last, rather squawkily, and Cyn was overwhelmed with fondness for him.

"Hello," she reassured him.

After a gap of half a minute, Lou got his question over with. "Was that alright?"

"Yeah." What a bland word, an insult, a mere grunt. What could she tell him about something so recent and brief that her brain had hardly registered it? "Rather different from how it used to be," Cyn added in an undertone.

"When?"

"Fifteen years ago."

"Fifteen years ago I was taking my first holy communion in velvet knickerbockers."

Cyn cleared her throat. "I meant with other men."

"I know." Lou turned his face up to the cracked ceiling. Silence covered them like a blanket, stifling the words. But if he didn't ask these questions now they would hammer in his head. "How different, exactly?"

Her face was angled into the pillow. What she said was muffled and he had to ask her to repeat it. "Not different enough," Cyn said at last.

"I'm sorry. I mean, that's fine. No sweat." What was he rabbiting on about? There was sweat everywhere, cooling the sheets against them like a mummy's wrappings.

It wasn't bright enough for Lou to see her eyes, but he could feel their gaze on his skin. "It's not you, it's me," she said, as if to a child. "You're very different from them, you make a totally different... shape. But I'm afraid I still can't quite see it."

He lay still, then scratched his ear. Why was he feeling bleak when it was such a relief? The things he had been dreading, ever since he woke up, were enthusiasm, romance, or a dreadfully earnest renegotiation of the terms.

Lou exhaled a quick prayer to the god he didn't believe in anymore. What he would have liked to say to the woman breathing beside him was a simple thanks that she seemed to have got about as much as he did out of the whole business and no more. But some things couldn't be said, even between friends. "Tea?" he asked, leaning up on one elbow.

"Please."

It took two months for them to feel safe enough to curl up on a sofa together. Lou's sofa this time, to avoid memories. It was May, and the sun sifted across the cushions. When he took her hand this time there was a layer of airiness between their bodies; it cushioned them, saved their nerves from jarring. They kept talking. Lou delivered a rant, punctuated with laughter, about the Rainbow's Artistic Director, who was so paranoid about

Clause 28 that he had instructed Lou to paint over the giants' moustaches and bandanas in case the Council withdrew funding. By the end of an argument about the Labour Party, Cyn decided that the electricity between them had been earthed and laid to rest. It felt so wonderfully ordinary, her hand lying on his. Laying her head back on one of Lou's granny's cushions, she decided she wouldn't have to unearth that "Bi Any Other Name" badge after all.

Lou watched her eyelids float in a sea of tiny lines. "Your accent's coming back these days, you know," he remarked.

"It is not!'

"Listen to yourself. "Tis an' all," he added in a stage-Oirish quaver.

She grinned and slid farther down the sofa arm, putting her boots up on his jeans. "Must be your evil influence."

If he didn't push it now he mightn't get another chance. "They say it's getting better over there, Cyn-ful."

"Don't they always."

"Ah but seriously. The Government are finally going to have to make us legal; they've promised to bring in an equal age of consent by July."

"Speak for yourself, I was never illegal."

"They'd have to get you for general indecency."

"They'd have to catch me first."

Lou rapped on her soles. "Stop messing. Why don't you come home with me at the end of June for Pride?"

Cyn opened one eye.

"Dublin has its very own Pride March now, isn't that the cutest thing?"

Her eye shut. "Dublin's not home. I grew up a hundred and fifty miles away. I've been to Manchester more often than Dublin."

"Well, think of it as a halfway point, then. Halfway between the Rainbow Centre and your parish hall."

The cushion dropped to the floor. "I'd rather think about tandoori chicken. Come on, my treat."

Lou followed her down the stairwell. The sun was pale yellow, snagged on a city spire; fingers of cloud stroked it as they passed. "I just can't believe in an Irish Pride March," Cyn commented, as they crossed the street to avoid a knot of skinheads. "It'd be a contradiction in terms. Pride is sun on the lions in Trafalgar Square and bobbies in helmets and that transvestite dressed up as Margaret Thatcher."

"What a traditionalist you are, for a deviant."

The point struck home. Cyn's walk slowed; her fists went deeper into her pockets. "Where'd we stay, if we did, which we won't?"

"I'll find a nice queer B&B in Dublin. Separate rooms, I assure you."

"But of course." She grabbed his hand, gave it a quick and only partly mocking kiss.

"It'll all be so different from how you remember it."

"How different exactly?"

"Let me guess what you're going to say: 'not different enough'?"

He caught the edge of a sheepish grin, as she turned her face away.

"Cyn, it's a new decade. Condom machines — "

" — much good that does me — '

" — a female president up in the Park. How about if I pay the price of your ticket if you're not entirely satisfied?"

"You couldn't afford to, unless you've been turning tricks in your lunchbreaks."

"I know," sighed Lou, "but didn't it sound impressive?" The campness left his tone. "Listen, you have to come back with me. If I went with English mates they wouldn't understand. Ireland's growing up, we have to be there."

"Oh really? Puberty is not a pretty sight. Tantrums and spots," Cyn reminded him, folding her arms across her jacket.

"Think of it more like a gorgeous teenager, with very soft eyelashes."

"Paedophile."

He pulled a hideous leer.

Cyn yawned as they turned the corner onto the high street. "I don't know, Lou-Lou, the very idea makes me tired. Wake me up when Ireland starts consenting to us instead of kicking us in the teeth."

"Any day now," he promised her, doubtfully.

"I'll believe it when I see it."

"You'll never see it unless you believe it a bit."

They wandered down the street past the restaurant, past the pub, coming to no conclusion. Like tails of cloud, their voices winding around and in and out.

Biographical Notes

SARA BERKELEY was born in Dublin in 1967. Since graduating from Trinity College, she has divided her time between America and London, where she curently lives. She published one collection of stories, *The Swimmer in the Deep Blue Dream*, in Ireland and Canada and her third collection of poetry is being co-published by New Island Books and Bloodaxe Books in 1994.

ROSITA BOLAND was born in Co Clare in 1965. After graduating from Trinity College she lived for periods in Australia and London, before returning to Ireland to research and write her account of hiking the entire Irish coastline alone, over three months in winter, *Sea Legs*. She has published one collection of poetry, *Muscle Creek*, and is currently working and travelling in Europe.

DERMOT BOLGER was born in Dublin, where he now lives, in 1959. A novelist (*The Journey Home, Emily's Shoes, The Woman's Daughter*), poet and playwright (*A Dublin Quartet, Penguin, 1992*), he founded the Raven Arts Press and has edited many anthologies, including *The Picador Book of Contemporary Irish Fiction.*

HARRY CLIFTON was born in Dublin in 1952, but has lived and worked for extended periods in Africa and the Far East, in between spells in Ireland. Most recently, with his wife Deirdre Madden, he has lived in Italy and London. He is the author of five collections of poems, including *The Desert Route: Selected Poems 1973-88.*

EMMA DONOGHUE was born in Dublin in 1969 and studied in UCD before moving to Cambridge to research a PhD on 18th century literary friendships. Her play, *I know My Own Heart: A Lesbian Regency Romance*, has been produced in Cambridge and Dublin, and she has two novels set in contemporary Ireland due from Hamish Hamilton in 1994 and 1995.

AIDAN HYNES was born in Castlebar, Co Mayo in 1956. He worked in various jobs from labouring to bartending before graduating from UCG. He taught adult literacy in Galway before emigrating to the USA. Married, he teaches in a New York high school and is secretary of the Irish Emigrants Vote Compaign.

TONY KEILY was born in Kobe, Japan in 1960. As a child he lived in Germany and England, before going to school in Kildare and University in Cork. Since 1983 he has lived in Barcelona.

COLUM McCANN was born in Dublin twenty seven years ago. He graduated from the University of Texes and now teaches in Japan. He has received the Sunday Tribune Hennessy Literary Award and an Arts Council of Ireland bursary, and his début collection of stories will be published by Phoenix House in 1994.

DEIRDRE MADDEN was born in Antrim in 1960. With her husband Harry Clifton she has lived in Italy (where her third novel, *Remembering Light and Stone* is set) and now in London. Her other books are *Hidden Symptoms* and *The Birds of the Innocent Wood.*

MARTIN MEENAN was born in Derry in 1959, moved to Bristol in 1978 and has lived in London since 1981. His work has been published in *Passages*, and he received second prize in the Francis McManus Short Story Competition in 1991.

HELENA MULKERNS was born in Dublin and lived in Spain and France before moving to New York, where, as a freelance journalist, her work has been published in *Rolling Stone, Irish Edition, New York Perspectives*, etc. She also writes for *The Irish Echo* newspaper and corresponds from New York for *Hot Press* and *The Irish Times*. His first fiction appeared in *The Sunday Tribune* and she is currenly completing a collection of stories.

JOSEPH O'CONNOR was born in Dublin in 1963 and lives in London, from where he travels widely in America and Spain. He has published two novels, a collection of stories, *True Believers*, and a study of the Irish poet, Charlie Donnelly, *Even the Olives are Bleeding*.

COLM O'GAORA was born in Dublin in 1966 and now works in London. His début collection of stories, *Giving Ground*, was published by Jonathan Cape in 1993.

MICHAEL O'LOUGHLIN was born in Dublin in 1958. Since graduating from Trinity College, he has lived abroad, firstly in Barcelona and, in recent years, in Amsterdam. He has published one collection of short stories, plus volumes of poetry, translations and critical essays. His new and selected poems is being co-published by New Island Books/Littlewood Arc in 1994.

GLENN PATTERSON was born in Belfast in 1961 and now lives in Manchester. He has published two novels, *Burning Your Own* and *Fat Lad*. This extract is from a new novel, set in Euro Disney.

EAMONN WALL was born in Enniscorthy, Co Wexford in 1955. He emigrated to the USA in 1982, and lived in New York, and now — with his wife and two children — in Omaha, Nebraska, where he teaches at Creighton University. His poetry and essays have been widely published in Ireland and America, and this is his first published fiction.

Acknowledgements

Where We Live and the extract from *A Ship Came from Valparaiso*, copyright © Harry Clifton, 1993. Reprinted with permission of the author.

Fishing the Sloe-Black River (to be published as part of a début collection by Phoenix House in 1994) copyright © Colum McCann, 1993. Reprinted with permission of the author and Sheil Land Associates Ltd.

Traditional Music by Michael O'Loughlin, from *The Inside Story*, first published by Raven Arts Press. © Michael O'Loughlin, 1989. Reprinted with permission of the author and The Raven Arts Press.

Extract from *Black Night at Big Thunder Mountain* (a novel in progress to be published by Chatto and Windus, copyright © Glenn Patterson, 1993. Printed with permission of Curtis Brown Group Ltd., London.

Extract from *Remembering Light and Stone* by Deirdre Madden. First published by Faber and Faber. Copyright © Deirdre Madden, 1992. Reprinted with permission.

Strands copyright © Tony Keily, 1993. Reprinted with permission of the author.

The Journey Back copyright © Aidan Hynes, 1993. Reprinted with permission of the author.

Four Pictures by Danny Maloney copyright © Eamonn Wall, 1993. Reprinted with permission of the author.